AUTHENTIC TRANSCRIPTIONS WITH NOTES AND TABLATURE

Take Off Your Pants And Jacket

Music transcriptions by Pete Billmann, Jeff Jacobson and Paul Pappas

International Music Publications Limited
Griffin House, 161 Hammersmith Road, London W6 8BS, England

Visit Hal Leonard Online at
www.halleonard.com

ATTICUS

Anthem Part II

Words and Music by Tom De Longe, Mark Hoppus and Travis Barker

A5
F5
C5

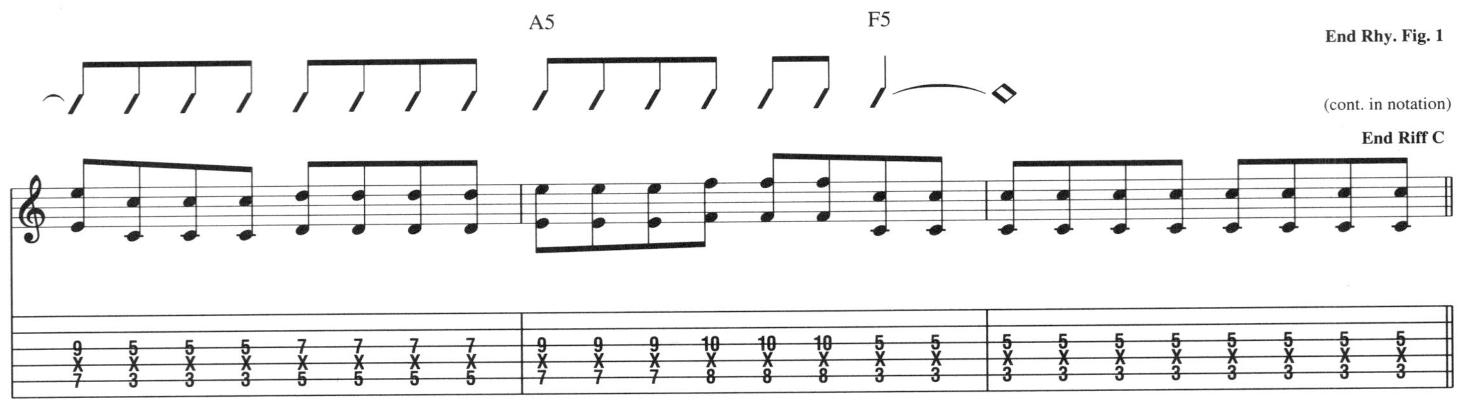
A5
F5
End Rhy. Fig. 1
(cont. in notation)
End Riff C

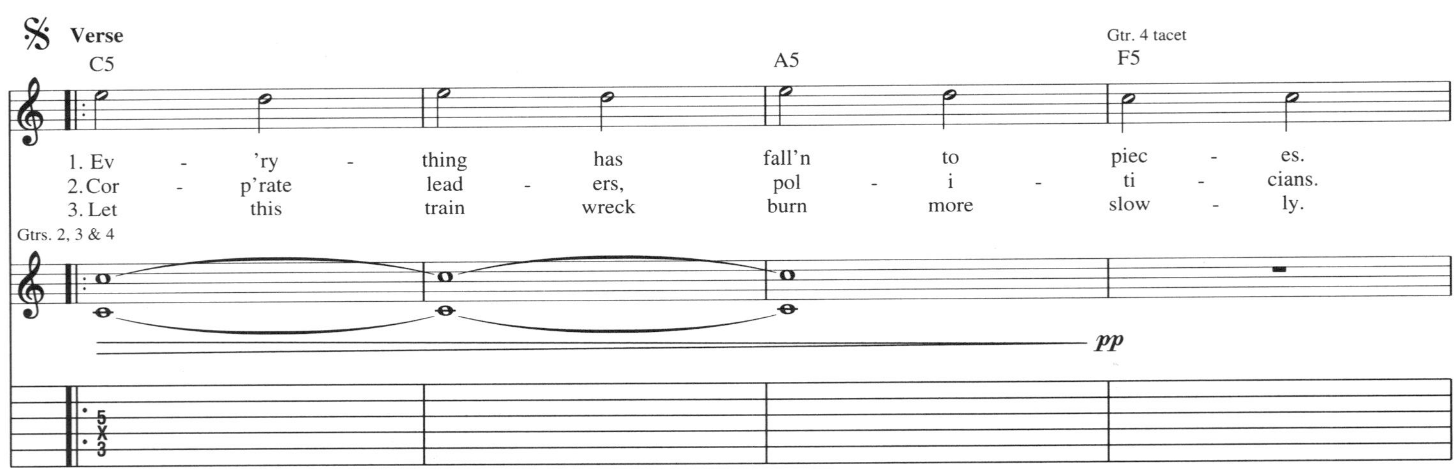
Verse
C5
A5
Gtr. 4 tacet
F5
1. Ev - 'ry - thing has fall'n to piec - es.
2. Cor - p'rate lead - ers, pol - i - ti - cians.
3. Let this train wreck burn more slow - ly.
Gtrs. 2, 3 & 4
pp

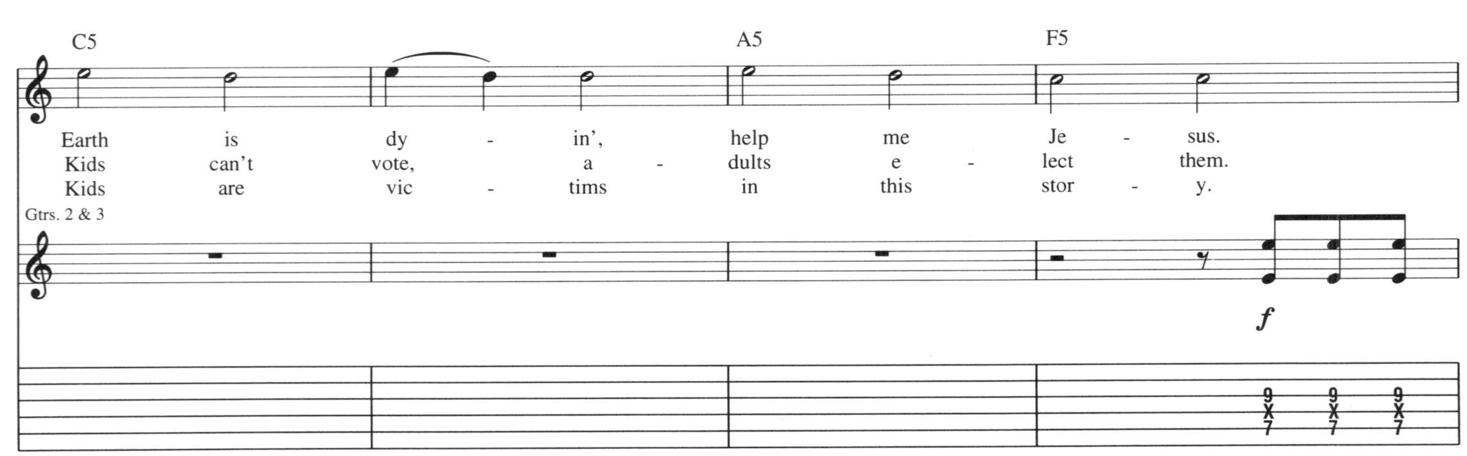
C5
A5
F5
Earth is dy - in', help me Je - sus.
Kids can't vote, a - dults e - lect them.
Kids are vic - tims in this stor - y.
Gtrs. 2 & 3
f

C5
A5
F5
We need guid - ance, we've been mis - led.
Laws that rule the school and work - place,
Drown the youth with use - less warn - ings.
P.M.
Young and hos - tile, but not stu - pid.
signs that cau - tion six - teen's un - safe.
Teen - age rules, they're fucked and bor - ing.
1.
Gtrs. 2 & 3 tacet
* Gtr. 5
Riff D
G5
mf
let ring throughout
End Riff D
* Bass arr. for gtr.
2.
Gtr. 5: w/ Riff D
(Ah.)
We real - ly
Chorus
C/E
E
open
Rhy. Fig. 2
Gtrs. 2 & 3
End Rhy. Fig. 2
need to see this through. We nev - er
Gtr. 4
Riff E
End Riff E

Gtrs. 2, 3 & 4: w/ Rhy. Fig. 2 & Riff E
C/E
F5
C5
G5
want - ed to be a - bused. We'll nev - er
A5
E
6
open
F5
C5
Gtrs. 2 & 3
P.M.
give up, it's no
Gtr. 4
To Coda 2
To Coda 1
G5
A5
E
F5
Rhy. Fill 1
End Rhy. Fill 1
(2nd time, cont. in notation)
P.M.
use. If we're fucked up, you're to blame.
Interlude
Gtrs. 2, 3 & 4: w/ Rhy. Fig. 1 & Riff C
D.S. al Coda 1
(take 2nd ending)
C5
A5
F5
Coda 1
Interlude
Gtr. 4 tacet
Gtrs. 2 & 3 tacet
Gtrs. 2 & 3
pp

Bridge
A5
F5
C5
A5
F5
Ev - 'ry - thing has fall'n to piec - es.
C5/G
Ev - 'ry - thing has fall'n to piec - es.
Gtr. 1
mp
D.S.S. al Coda 2
Ev - 'ry - thing has fall'n to... We real - ly
Coda 2
Gtrs. 2 & 3: w/ Rhy. Fill 1
A5
F5
Outro
Gtr. 2: w/ Riff B (3 3/4 times)
C5
D5
A5
F5
we're fucked up, you're to blame.
Gtrs. 3 & 4
2nd time, Gtr. 1: w/ Riff A (1 3/4 times)
C5
D5
A5
1.,2.
F5
3.
Fsus2
Gtrs. 2, 3 & 4
Gtr. 1
(cont. in slashes)

Online Songs

Words and Music by Tom De Longe, Mark Hoppus and Travis Barker

Interlude
Double-time feel
Gtr. 1 tacet
* Gtr. 2 (dist.)
A
D5/B
A/D
mf
** P.M.
*Doubled throughout
**P.M. on 6th string, next 8 meas.
E7(no3rd)
A
D5/B
A/D
D5/E
Verse
A5
2. Why do you still keep it a-
3. Why am I still hang-ing a-
if we can have an-oth-er
D5
F#5
E5
A5
round when you know it brings me down, I'm hat-ing ev-'ry-thing.
round when I know it brings me down, I'm hat-ing ev-'ry-thing.
day, I've got so much left to say, I'd tell you ev-'ry-thing.
And I
And you
And I'll
pp
Gtr. 2 tacet
D5
1.
F#5
E5
A5
know that you dat-ed oth-er guys, but I got-ta won-der why you'd leave it out for me.
are get-ting rides home in his car, you're mak-ing out in his front
laugh when I think a-bout the past. When I see you af-ter
Yeah!

2.
Chorus
F#5
E5
A5
D5
yard, I'm hat - ing ev - 'ry - thing.
class, you're hat - ing ev - 'ry - thing.
Please don't re - mind me, put your past be -
Gtr. 2
Rhy. Fig. 1
P.S.
hind me, it shines so bright it blinds me, I wish that this would end. And I am
End Rhy. Fig. 1
To Coda 1
To Coda 2
D.S. al Coda 1
(take 2nd ending)
Gtr. 2: w/ Rhy. Fig. 1
not fine, last night I saw you on - line. Your screen name used to be mine. Why can't we just pre - tend? 4. And
Coda 1
be mine. Why can't we just pre - tend? Please don't re -
Chorus
mind me, put your past be - hind me, it shines so bright it blinds me, I wish that this would end. And I am
Rhy. Fig. 2
End Rhy. Fig. 2
End double-time feel
Gtr. 2: w/ Rhy. Fig. 2
not fine, last night I saw you on - line. Your screen name used to be mine. Why can't we just pre - tend? And she said,

Bridge
F#5
D5
A5
E5
"Na, na, na, na, na, na, na, na, na, na, na, na, na." (I just for - got you were there.)
Gtr. 2
Rhy. Fig. 3
End Rhy. Fig. 3
Gtr. 2: w/ Rhy. Fig. 3
"Na, na, na, na, na, na, na, na, na, na, na, na, na." (I just for - got you were there.)
Rhy. Fig. 4
End Rhy. Fig. 4
"Na, na, na, na, na, na, na, na, na, na, na, na, na, na, na, na, na." (I just for - got you were there.)
Gtr. 2: w/ Rhy. Fig. 4
D.S.S. al Coda 2
"Na, na, na, na, na, na, na, na, na, na, na, na, na, na, na, na, na." Please don't re -
Coda 2
Outro-Chorus
Gtr. 2: w/ Rhy. Fig. 2 (1 1/2 times)
be mine. Why can't we just pre - tend? Please don't re - mind me, put your past be - hind me, it shines so bright it
blinds me, I wish that this would end. And I am not fine, last night I saw you on - line. Your screen name used to
be mine. Why can't we just pre - tend? And she said, "Na, na, na, na, na."

First Date

Words and Music by Tom De Longe, Mark Hoppus and Travis Barker

Gtr. 2: w/ Riff B
C
G
F
I'm just scared of what you think.
You make me ner-vous so I real-ly can't eat.
I dread the thought of our ver-y first kiss,
a tar-get that I'm prob-'ly gon-na miss.

Chorus
C5
G/B
A5
F5
G5
Let's go, don't wait, this night's al-most o-ver.
Gtrs. 1 & 2
Rhy. Fig. 2
End Rhy. Fig. 2

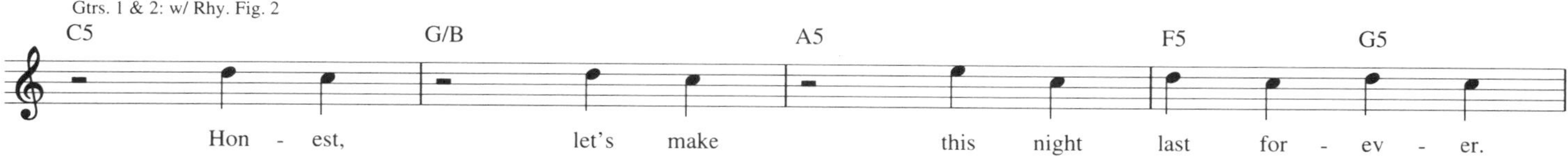
Gtrs. 1 & 2: w/ Rhy. Fig. 2
C5
G/B
A5
F5
G5
Hon-est, let's make this night last for-ev-er.

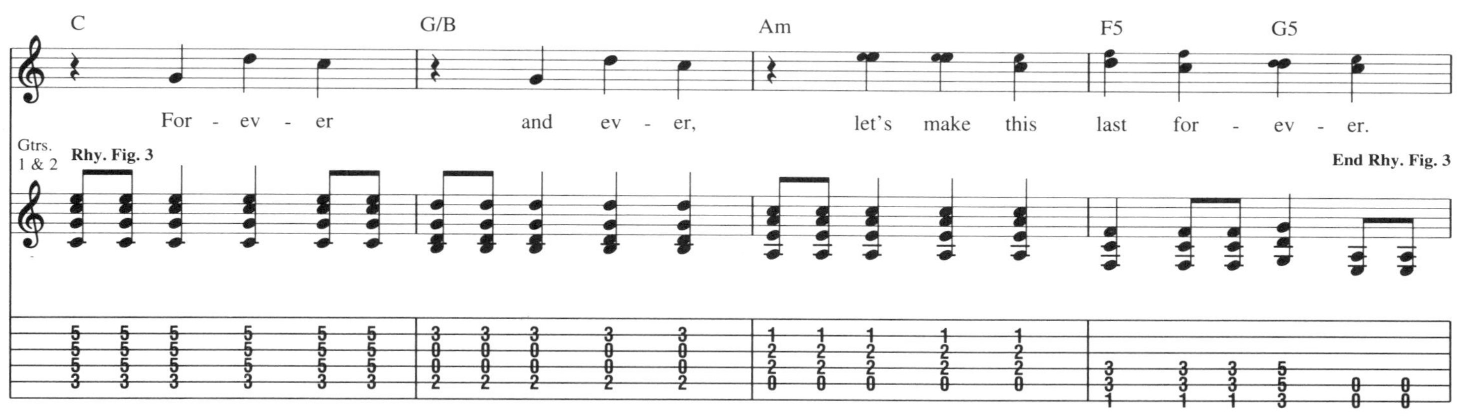
C
G/B
Am
F5
G5
For-ev-er and ev-er, let's make this last for-ev-er.
Gtrs. 1 & 2
Rhy. Fig. 3
End Rhy. Fig. 3

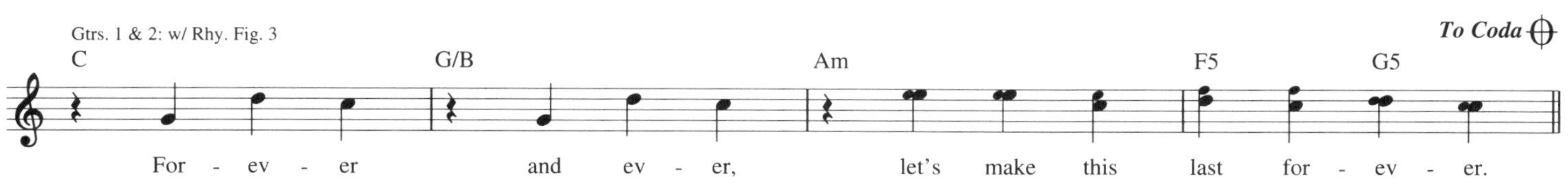
Gtrs. 1 & 2: w/ Rhy. Fig. 3
To Coda
C
G/B
Am
F5
G5
For-ev-er and ev-er, let's make this last for-ev-er.

1.
Interlude
Gtr. 1: w/ Riff A
Gtr. 2: w/ Rhy. Fig. 1 (2 times)
C5
D5
F5
G5
C5
D5
F5
G5

2.
Guitar Solo
Gtr. 2
C5
C/E
F5
G5
P.M.
Riff C
End Riff C
Gtr. 2: w/ Riff C (4 times)
Gtr. 1
3rd time, D.S. al Coda
Play 3 times
Coda
Gtr. 1: w/ Riff A
Gtr. 2: w/ Rhy. Fig. 3 (2 times)
C
G/B
Am
For - ev - er and ev - er, let's make this last for - ev - er.
For - ev - er and ev - er, let's make this last for - ev - er.
Gtr. 2
Gtr. 1

Happy Holidays, You Bastard

Words and Music by Tom De Longe, Mark Hoppus and Travis Barker

Gtr. 1: w/ Rhy. Fig. 3
B5
F#5
E5
I'll nev - er talk to you a - gain.
cock. E - jac - u - late in - to a
To Coda
B5
F#5
E5
F#5
I'll nev - er talk to you a - gain, I'll nev - er talk to you a -
sock.) 2. It's La - bor
Verse
Gtr. 1: w/ Rhy. Fig. 1 (2 times)
B5
F#5
gain. and my grand - pa just ate sev - en fuck - in' hot dogs. La - bor
Day
B5
F#5
Day and my grand - pa just ate sev - en fuck - in' hot dogs and he
Gtr. 1: w/ Rhy. Fig. 2
G#5
E5
shit, shit, shit his pants. He's al - ways fuck - in' shit - in' his pants and
D.S. al Coda
B5
F#5
E5
F#5
I'll nev - er talk to you a - gain.
(Un - less your dad will suck me
Coda
E5
F#5
B5
gain, I'll nev - er talk to you a - gain.

Story of a Lonely Guy

Words and Music by Tom De Longe, Mark Hoppus and Travis Barker

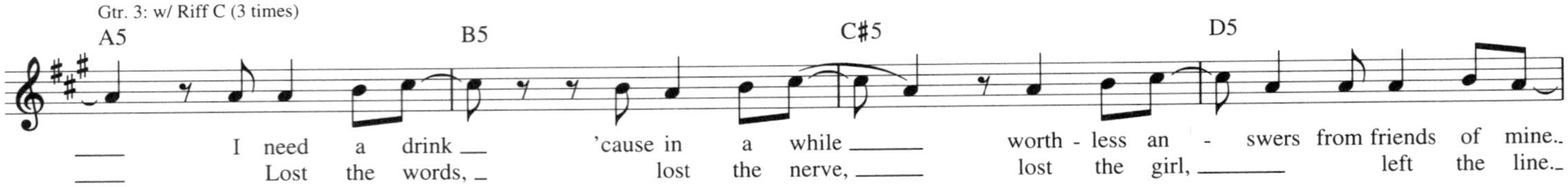
Gtr. 3: w/ Riff C (3 times)
A5
B5
C#5
D5
I need a drink 'cause in a while worth - less an - swers from friends of mine.
Lost the words, lost the nerve, lost the girl, left the line.

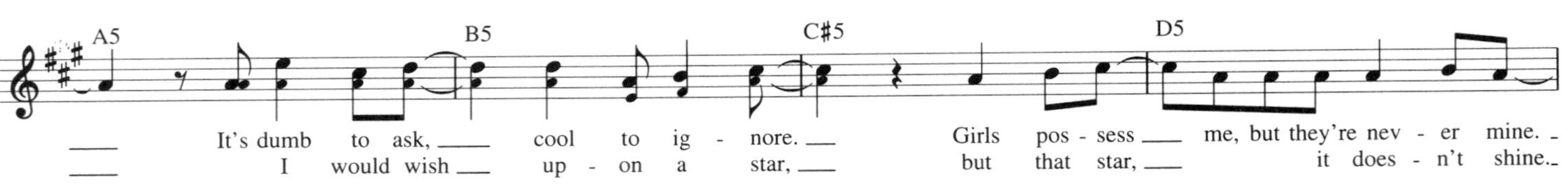
A5
B5
C#5
D5
It's dumb to ask, cool to ig - nore. Girls pos - sess me, but they're nev - er mine.
I would wish up - on a star, but that star, it does - n't shine.

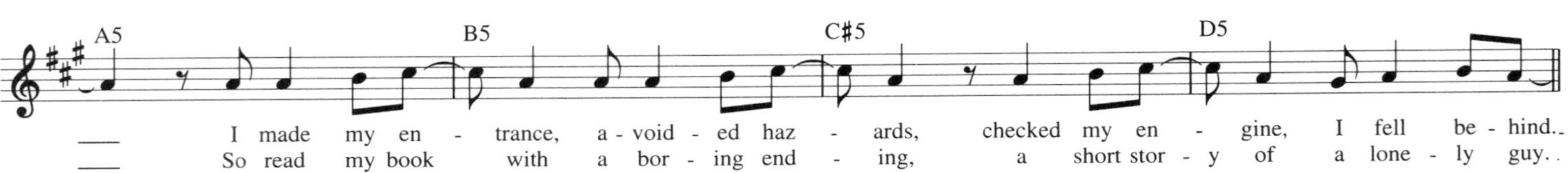
A5
B5
C#5
D5
I made my en - trance, a - void - ed haz - ards, checked my en - gine, I fell be - hind.
So read my book with a bor - ing end - ing, a short stor - y of a lone - ly guy.

Pre-Chorus

A/C# D5 A5 Esus4

(Da, da, da, da, da, da, da, da, da, da, da, da, {I / who} fell be - hind. / da.

Gtr. 2

Riff D ... End Riff D

mf

Gtr. 3

pp

Gtr. 2: w/ Riff D
A/C#
D5
A5
Esus4
Da, da, da,
da, da, da,
da, da, da,
da, da, da, da.)
Gtr. 3
P.S.

Chorus

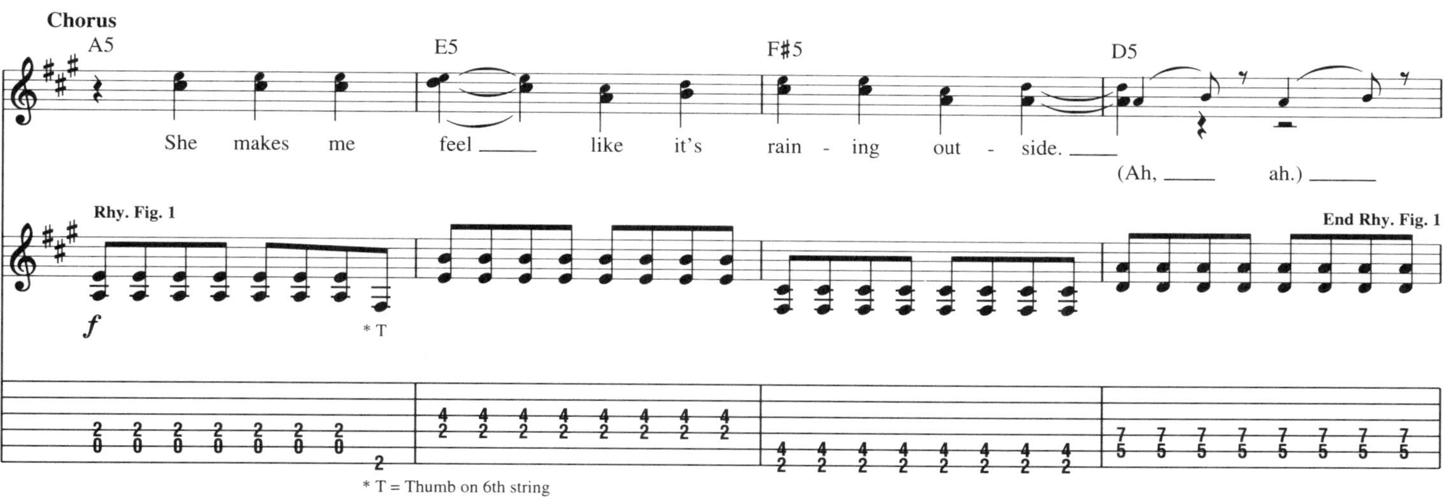
A5
E5
F#5
D5
She makes me feel like it's rain - ing out - side.
(Ah, ah.)
Rhy. Fig. 1
End Rhy. Fig. 1
* T
* T = Thumb on 6th string

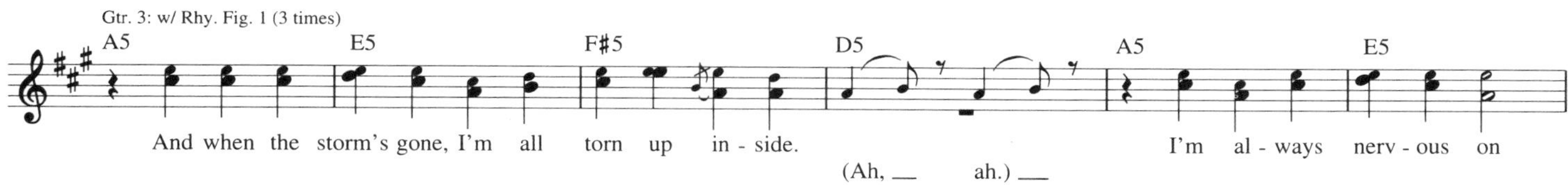
Gtr. 3: w/ Rhy. Fig. 1 (3 times)
A5
E5
F#5
D5
A5
E5
And when the storm's gone, I'm all torn up in - side.
(Ah, ah.)
I'm al - ways nerv - ous on

F#5
D5
A5
E5
F#5
D5
days like this like the prom.
I get too scared to move 'cause I'm a fuck - in' boy.

1.
Interlude

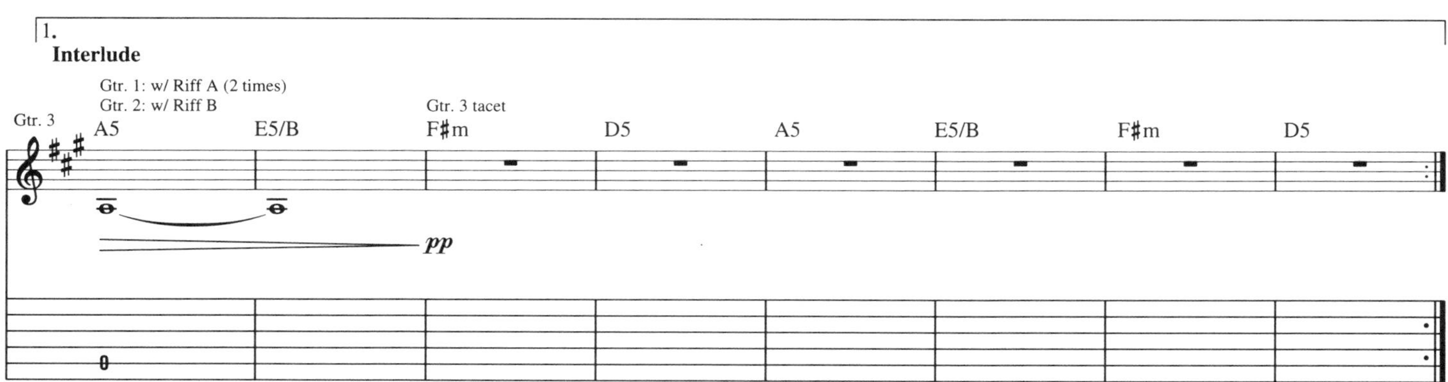
Gtr. 1: w/ Riff A (2 times)
Gtr. 2: w/ Riff B
Gtr. 3 tacet
Gtr. 3
A5
E5/B
F#m
D5
A5
E5/B
F#m
D5
pp

2. Interlude
Gtr. 2
A/C#
D5
E5
Gtr. 3
A/C#
D5
E5
Gtr. 3 tacet
Gtr. 2
A/C#
D5
Esus4
A/C#
D5

Pre-Chorus
Gtr. 2 tacet
Gtr. 3: w/ Rhy. Fig. 1 (2 times)
A5
E5
F♯5
D5
(Da, da, da, da, da, da, da, da, da, da, da, da, da.
A5
Voc. Fig. 1
E5
F♯5
D5
End Voc. Fig. 1
Da, da, da, da, da, da, da, da, da, da, da, da, da,)
Chorus
Bkgd. Voc.: w/ Voc. Fig. 1 (1st. 3 meas.)
Gtr. 3: w/ Rhy. Fig. 1 (3 3/4 times)
Bkgd. Voc.: w/ Voc. Fig. 1 (1st. 3 meas.)
She makes me feel like it's rain - ing out - side.
(Ah, ah.)
And when the storm's gone, I'm all torn up in - side.
(Ah, ah.)
* Gtr. 1: w/ Riff A (1 3/4 times)
Bkgd. Voc.: w/ Voc. Fig. 1 (2 times)
I'm al - ways nerv - ous on days like this like the prom.
* w/ slight dist.
I get too scared to move 'cause I'm still just a stu - pid, worth - less boy.
Gtr. 1
Gtr. 3

The Rock Show

Words and Music by Tom De Longe, Mark Hoppus and Travis Barker

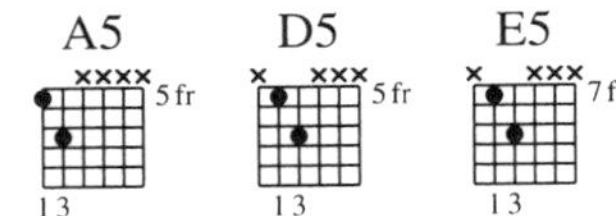

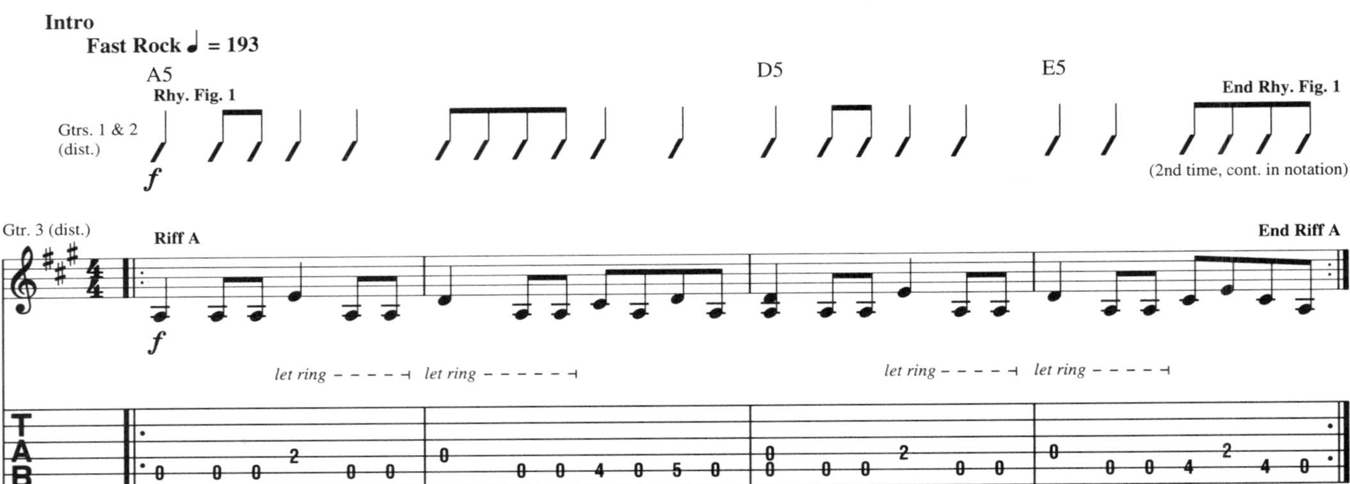

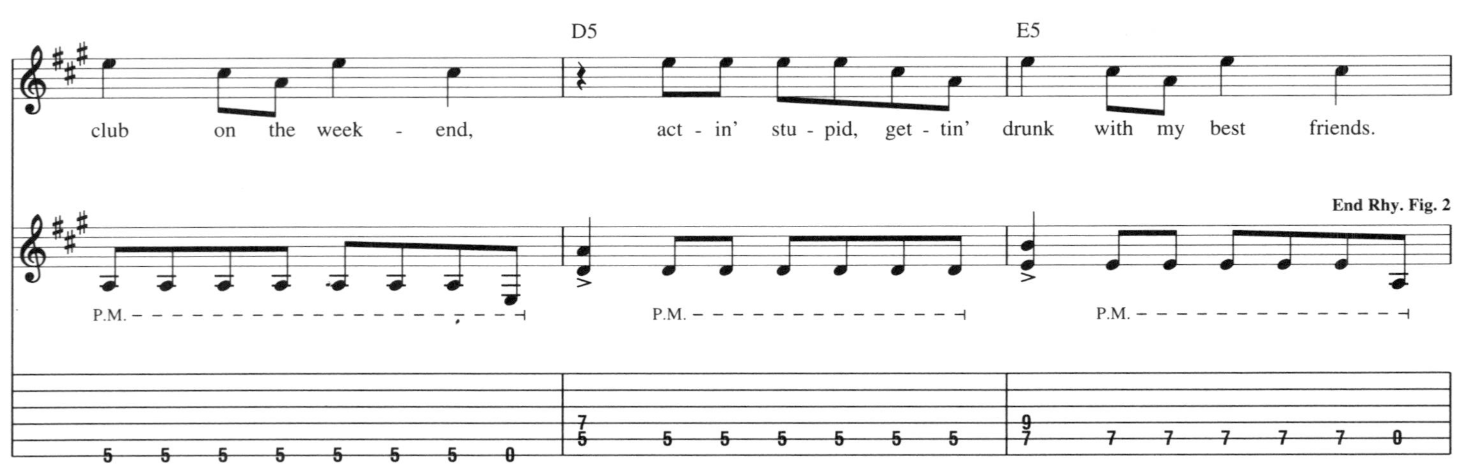

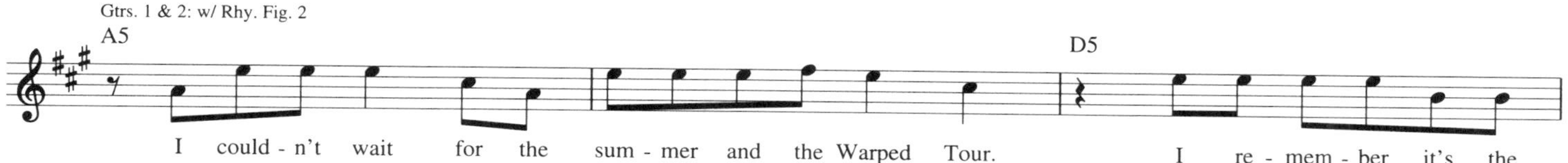
Gtrs. 1 & 2: w/ Rhy. Fig. 2
A5
D5
I could - n't wait for the sum - mer and the Warped Tour. I re - mem - ber it's the

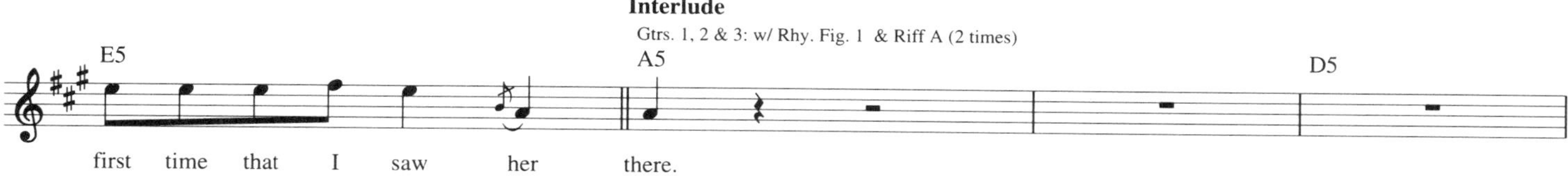
Interlude
Gtrs. 1, 2 & 3: w/ Rhy. Fig. 1 & Riff A (2 times)
E5
A5
D5
first time that I saw her there.

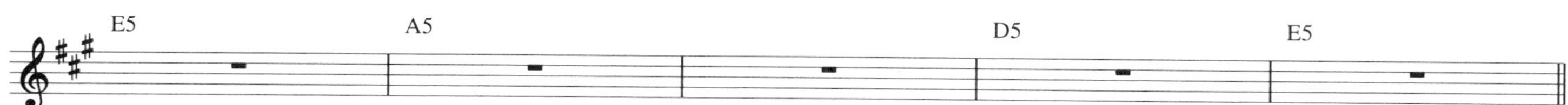
E5
A5
D5
E5

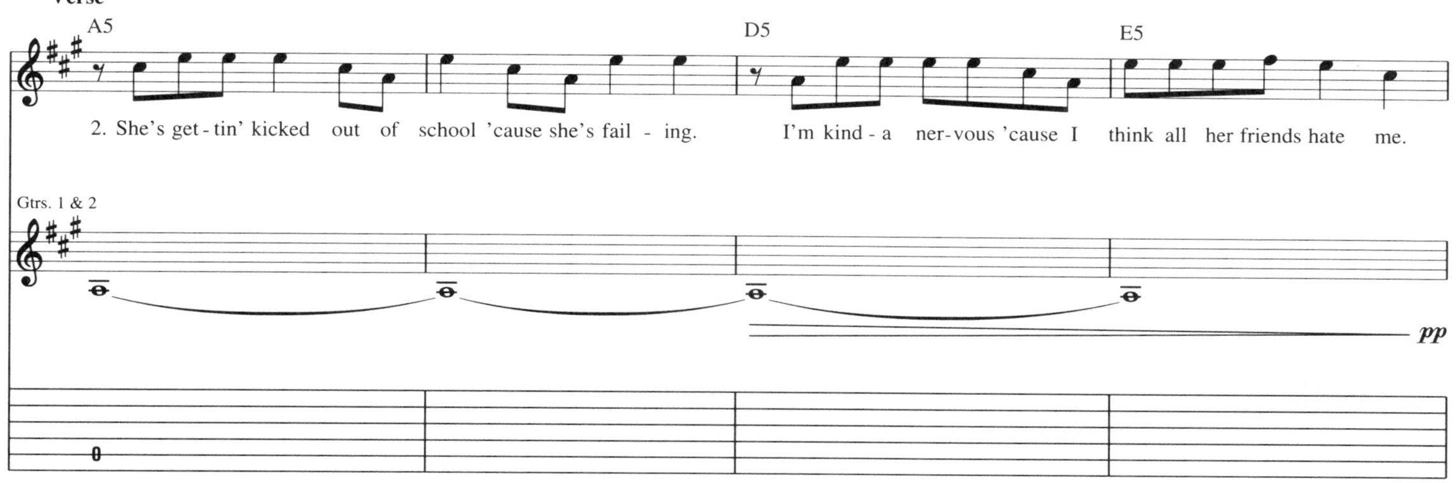
Verse
A5
D5
E5
2. She's get - tin' kicked out of school 'cause she's fail - ing. I'm kind - a ner - vous 'cause I think all her friends hate me.
Gtrs. 1 & 2
pp

A5
D5
E5
She's the one, she'll al - ways be there. She took my hand and that made it I swear be - cause I

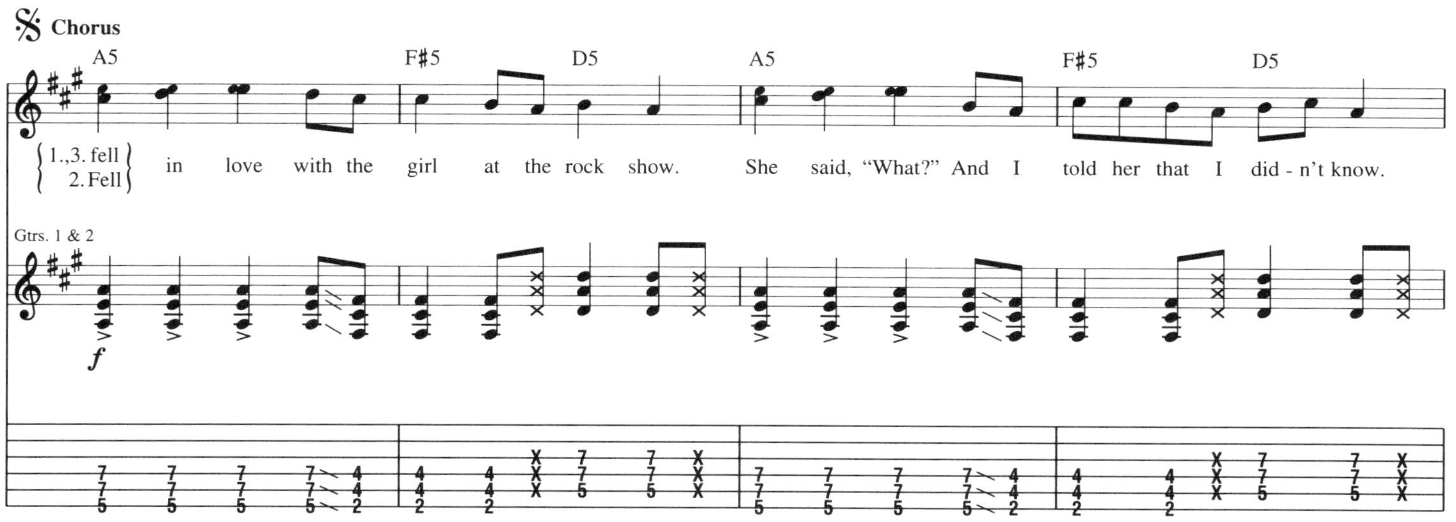
Chorus
A5
F#5
D5
A5
F#5
D5
1.,3. fell
2. Fell
in love with the girl at the rock show. She said, "What?" And I told her that I did - n't know.
Gtrs. 1 & 2
f

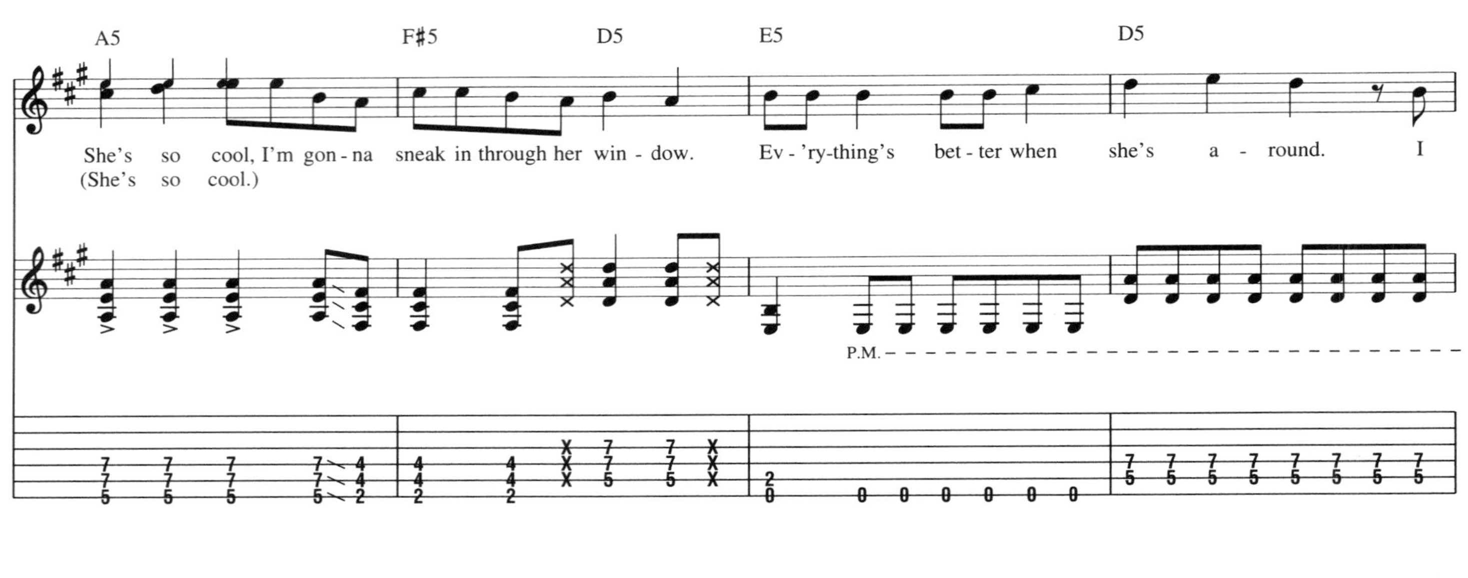
A5
F♯5
D5
E5
D5
She's so cool, I'm gon - na sneak in through her win - dow. Ev - 'ry-thing's bet - ter when she's a - round. I
(She's so cool.)
P.M.

To Coda 1
To Coda 2
E5
D5
E5
D5
A/C♯
can't wait 'til her par-ents go out of town. I fell in love with the girl at the rock show.
P.M.

Interlude

Gtrs. 1, 2 & 3: w/ Rhy. Fig. 1 & Riff A (2 times)
A5
D5
E5

Verse

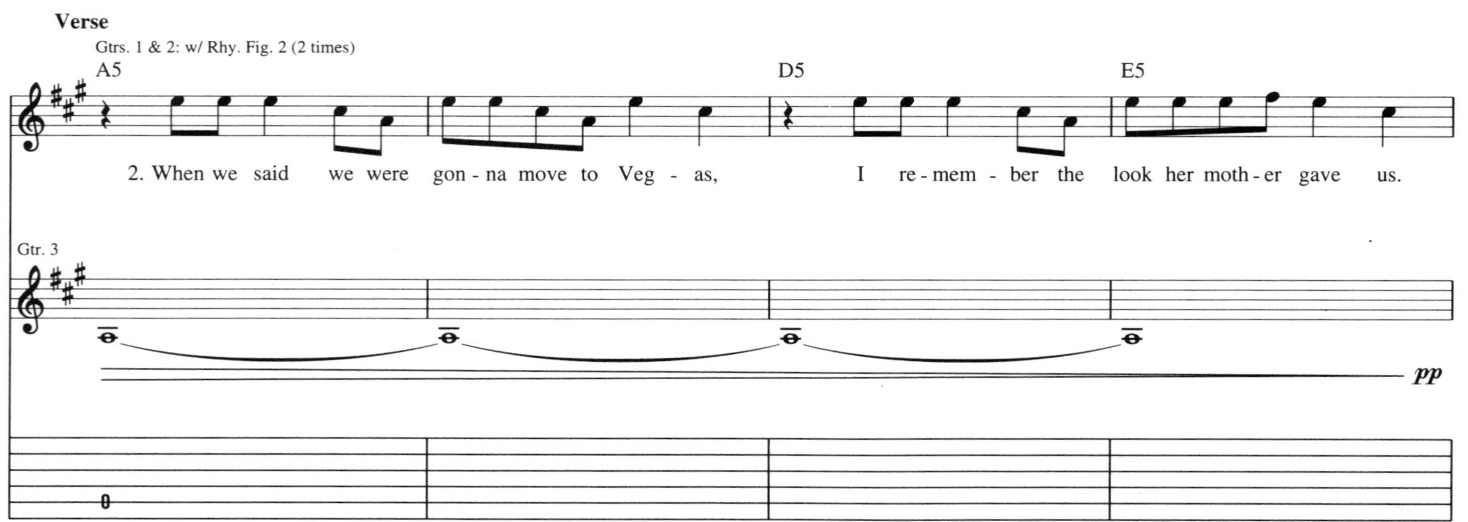
Gtrs. 1 & 2: w/ Rhy. Fig. 2 (2 times)
A5
D5
E5
2. When we said we were gon - na move to Veg - as, I re - mem - ber the look her moth - er gave us.
Gtr. 3
pp

D.S. al Coda 1

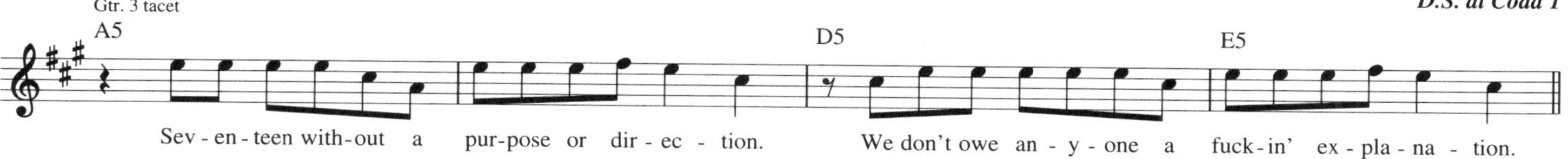
Gtr. 3 tacet
A5
D5
E5
Sev - en - teen with-out a pur-pose or dir - ec - tion. We don't owe an - y - one a fuck-in' ex - pla - na - tion.

Coda 1
Bridge
F#m
Dmaj7
Black and white pic - ture of her on my wall. I wait - ed
Gtr. 4 (clean)
Riff B
mf
let ring throughout

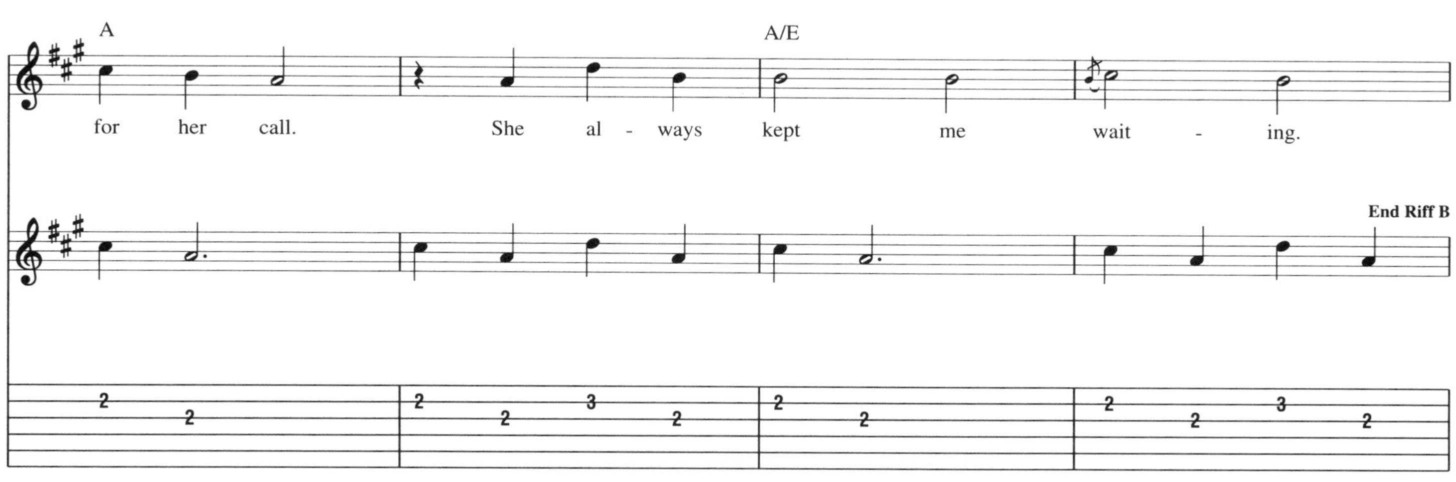
A
A/E
for her call. She al - ways kept me wait - ing.
End Riff B

Gtr. 4: w/ Riff B
F#m
Dmaj7
And if I ev - er got an - oth - er chance, I'd still ask
Gtrs. 1 & 2
mf

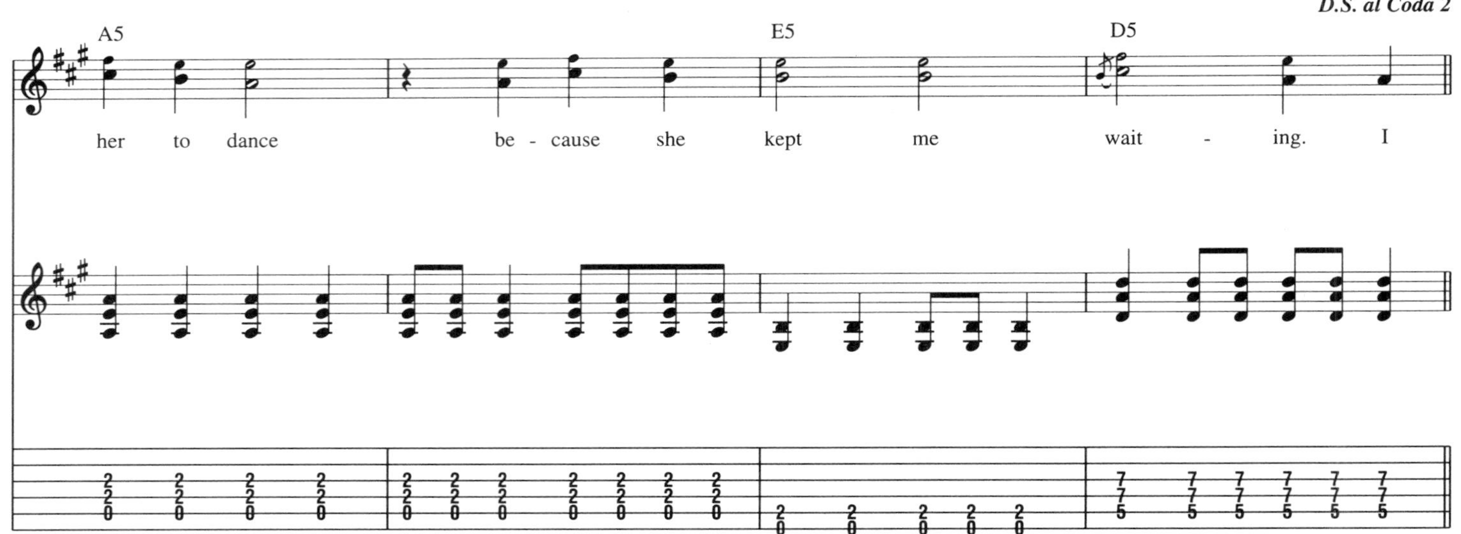
D.S. al Coda 2
A5
E5
D5
her to dance be - cause she kept me wait - ing. I

Coda 2

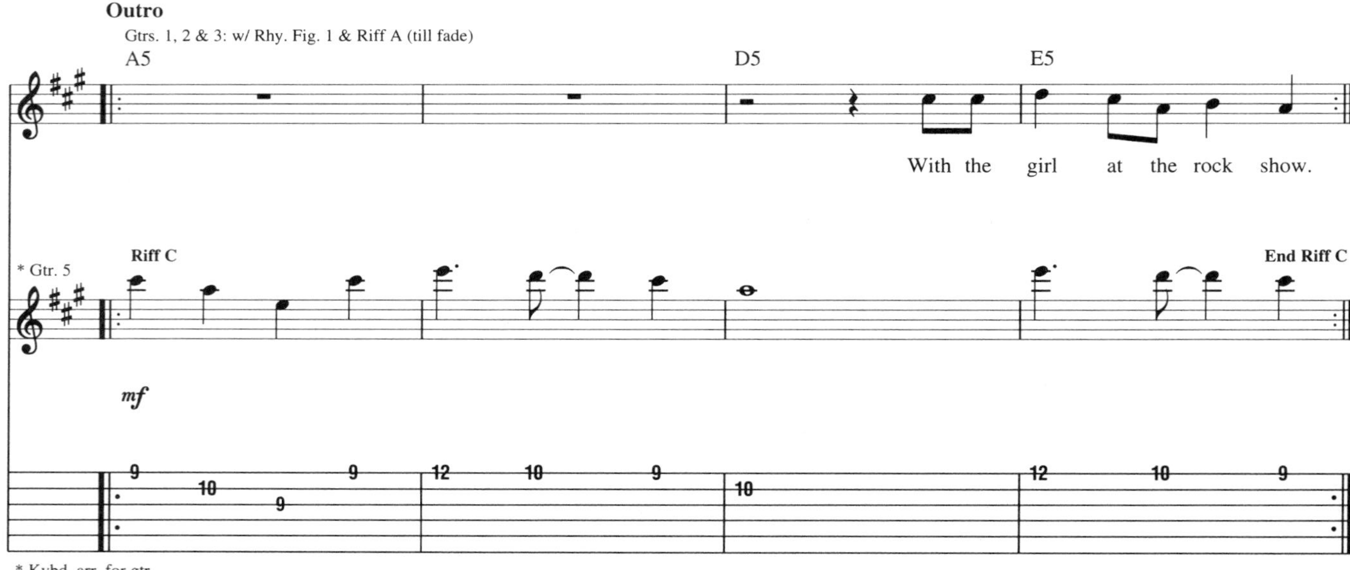
Outro
Gtrs. 1, 2 & 3: w/ Rhy. Fig. 1 & Riff A (till fade)
A5
D5
E5
With the girl at the rock show.
* Gtr. 5
Riff C
End Riff C
mf
* Kybd. arr. for gtr.

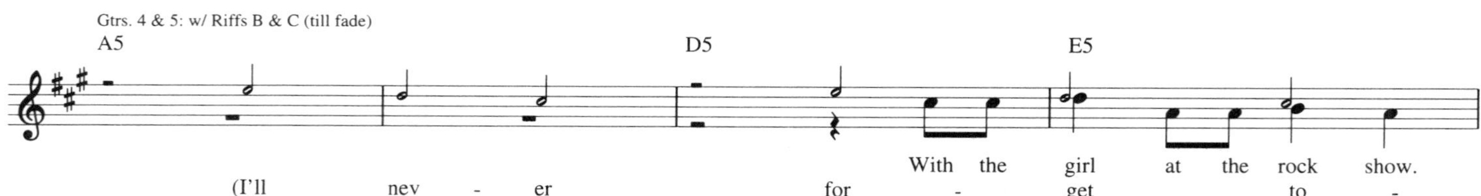
Gtrs. 4 & 5: w/ Riffs B & C (till fade)
A5
D5
E5
With the girl at the rock show.
(I'll nev - er for - get to -

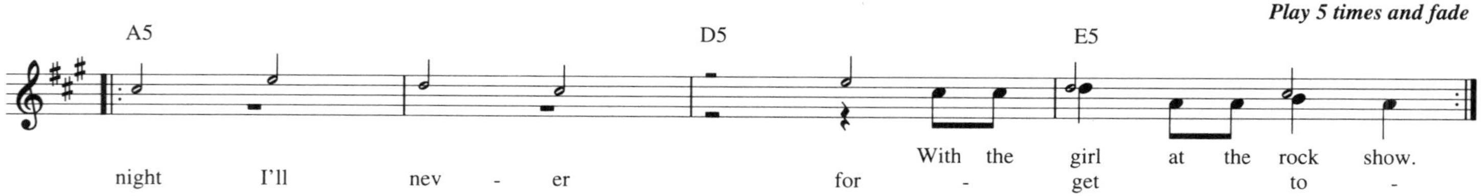
Play 5 times and fade
A5
D5
E5
With the girl at the rock show.
night I'll nev - er for - get to -

Stay Together for the Kids

Words and Music by Tom De Longe, Mark Hoppus and Travis Barker

Chorus
G5
D/F♯
So here's your hol - i - day,
hope you en -
Gtr. 2 (elec.)
Rhy. Fig. 2
End Rhy. Fig. 2
f w/ dist.
Gtr. 2: w/ Rhy. Fig. 2 (2 times)
joy it this time. You gave it all a - way, it was mine.
So when you're dead and gone, will you re -
mem-ber this night? Twen - ty years now lost, it's not right.
Gtr. 2
Interlude
Gtr. 1: w/ Riff A (2 times)
D D/C♯ Bm A5
Gtr. 2 tacet
Verse
D5
Bm7
2. Their an - ger hurts my ears, been run-nin' strong for sev - en years.
Gtr. 1
Riff B

Asus4
A5
Rath-er than fix the prob - lems they nev - er solve them. It makes no sense at all.
End Riff B
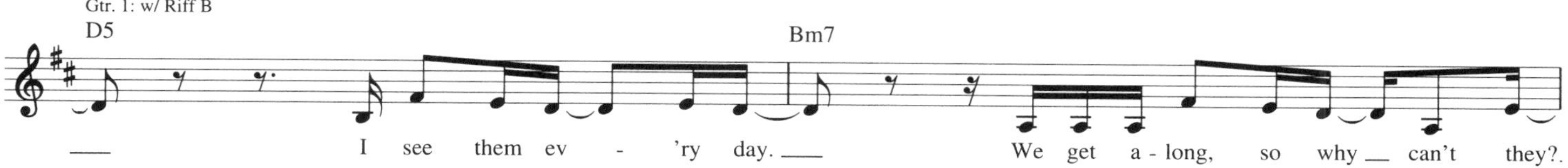
Gtr. 1: w/ Riff B
D5
Bm7
I see them ev - 'ry day. We get a - long, so why can't they?.
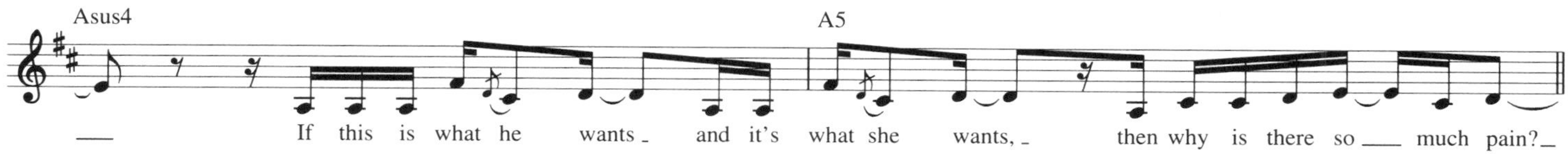
Asus4
A5
If this is what he wants and it's what she wants, then why is there so much pain?

Chorus

Gtr. 2: w/ Rhy. Fig. 2 (3 times)
G5
D/F#
G5
So here's your hol - i - day, hope you en - joy it this time. You gave it all a - way,

D/F#
G5
D/F#
it was mine. So when you're dead and gone, will you re -
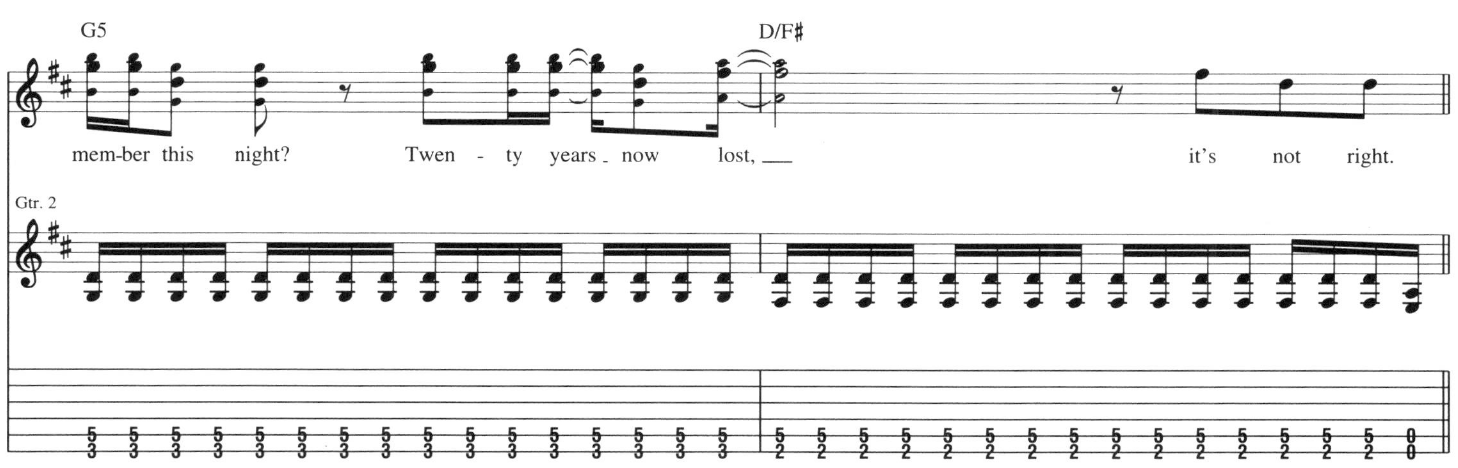
G5
D/F#
mem-ber this night? Twen - ty years now lost, it's not right.
Gtr. 2

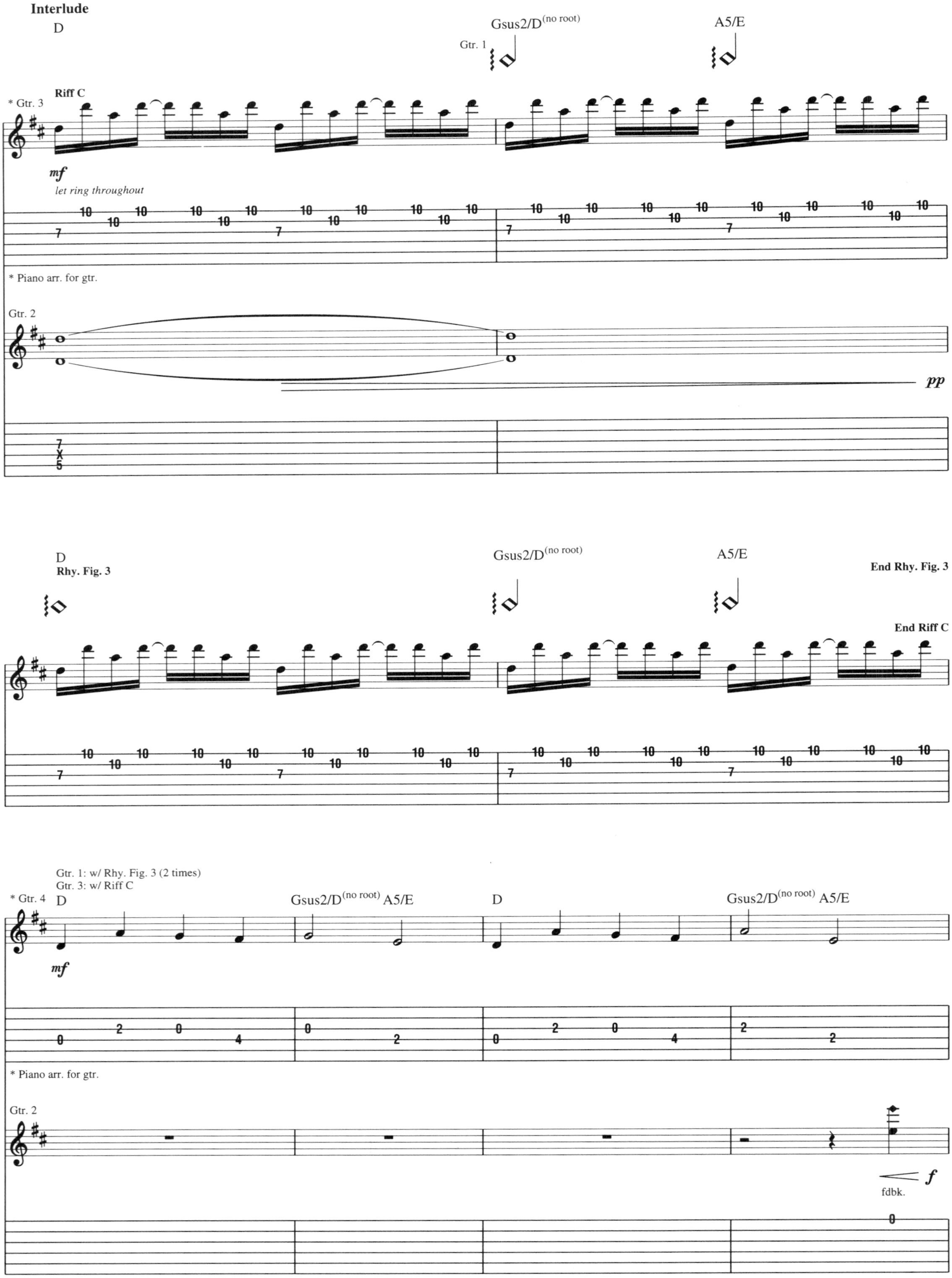

Interlude
D
Gsus2/D(no root)
A5/E
Gtr. 1
Riff C
* Gtr. 3
mf
let ring throughout
* Piano arr. for gtr.
Gtr. 2
pp
D
Rhy. Fig. 3
Gsus2/D(no root)
A5/E
End Rhy. Fig. 3
End Riff C
Gtr. 1: w/ Rhy. Fig. 3 (2 times)
Gtr. 3: w/ Riff C
* Gtr. 4
D
Gsus2/D(no root) A5/E
D
Gsus2/D(no root) A5/E
mf
* Piano arr. for gtr.
Gtr. 2
f
fdbk.

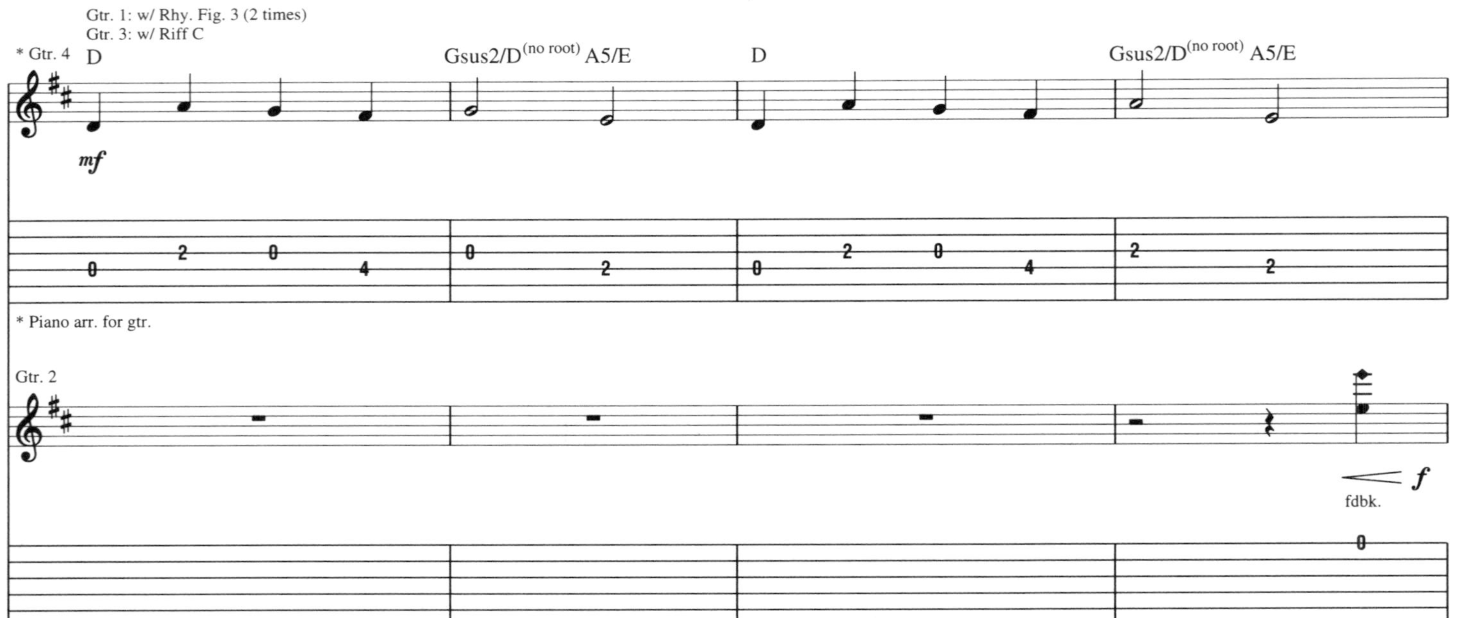

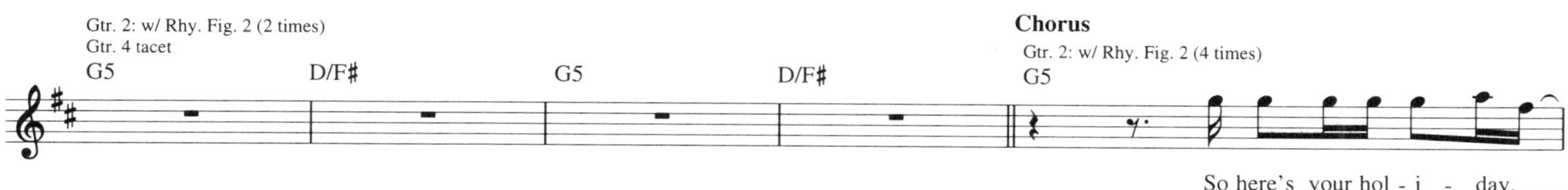
Gtr. 2: w/ Rhy. Fig. 2 (2 times)
Gtr. 4 tacet
G5
D/F#
G5
D/F#
Chorus
Gtr. 2: w/ Rhy. Fig. 2 (4 times)
G5
So here's your hol - i - day,

D/F#
G5
D/F#
hope you en - joy it this time. You gave it all a - way, it was mine.

G5
D/F#
G5
So when you're dead and gone, will you re - mem-ber this night? Twen - ty years now lost,

D/F#
Outro
Gtr. 2: w/ Rhy. Fig. 2 (till fade)
G5
D/F#
G5
it's not right. It's not right, it's not right, it's not right.

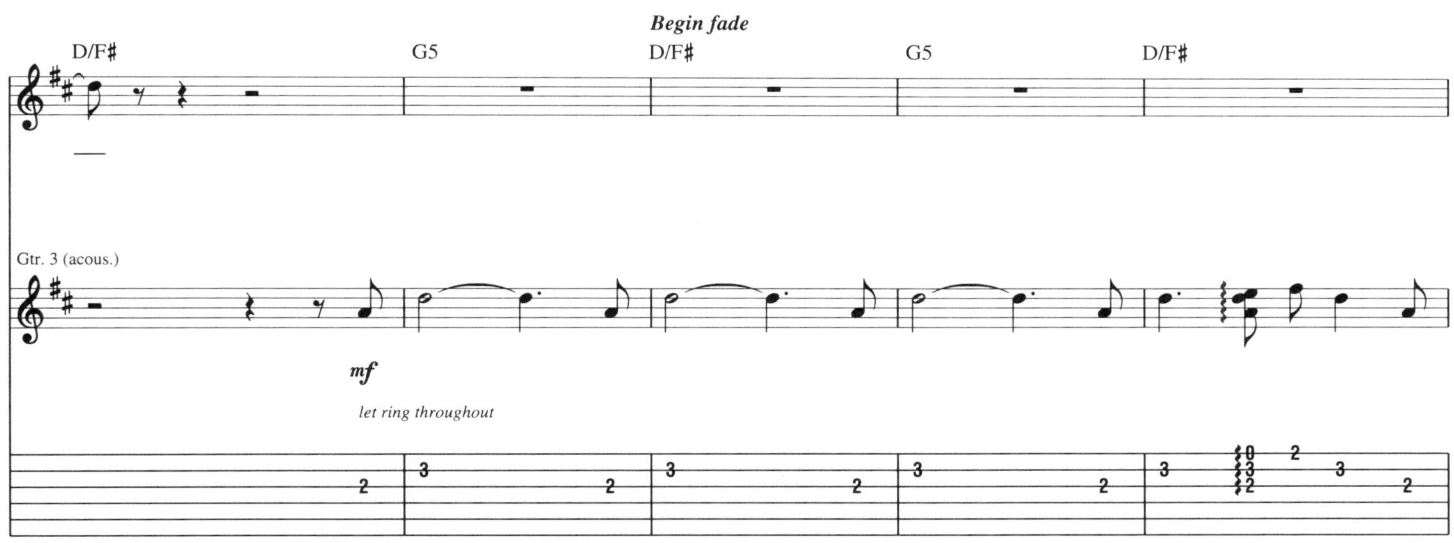
Begin fade
D/F#
G5
D/F#
G5
D/F#
Gtr. 3 (acous.)
mf
let ring throughout

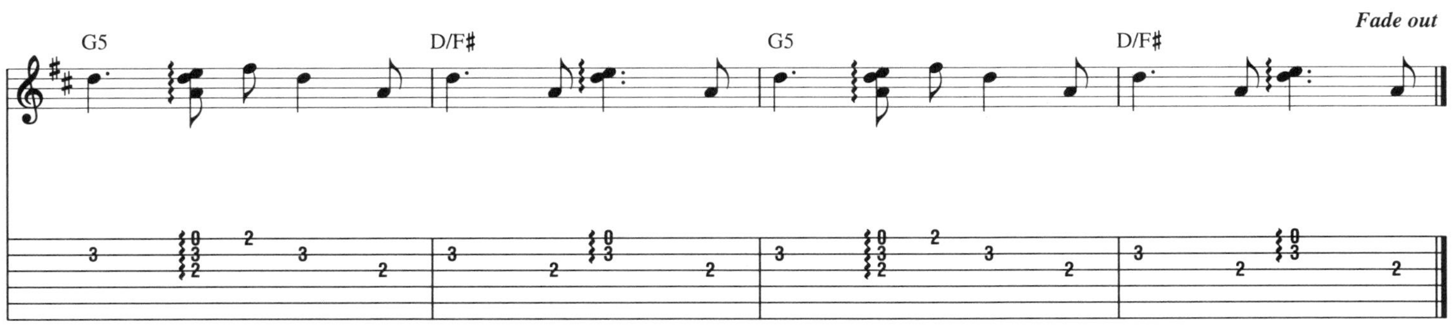
G5
D/F#
G5
D/F#
Fade out

Roller Coaster

Words and Music by Tom De Longe, Mark Hoppus and Travis Barker

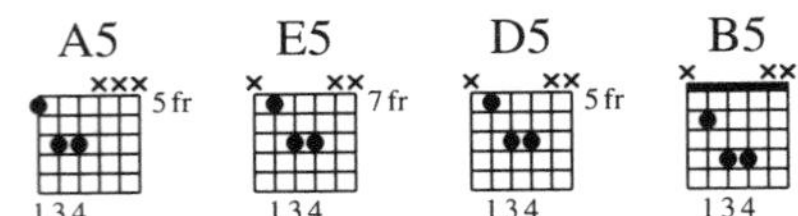

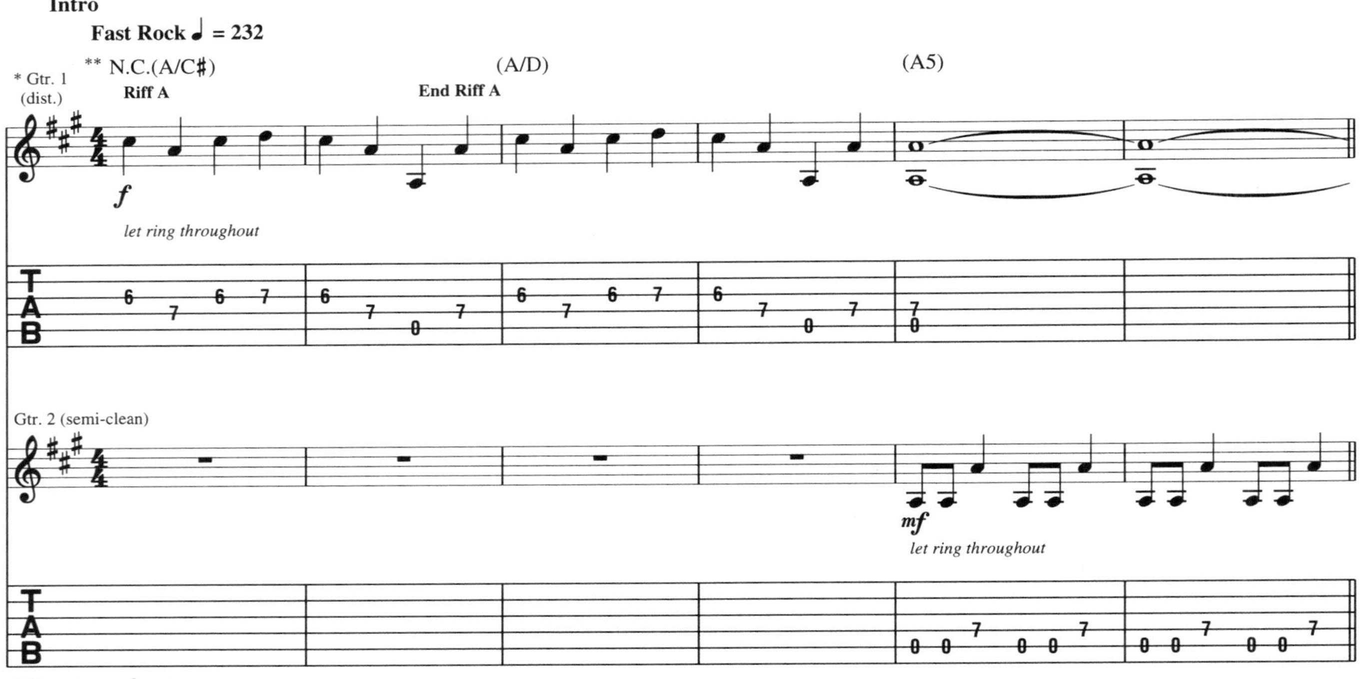

* Two gtrs. arr. for one.
** Chord symbols reflect overall harmony.

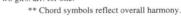

Gtr. 1 tacet
(D5)
(B7(no3rd))
(D5)
find - ing strength to call and ask her.
Gtr. 2
End Riff B
Gtr. 2: w/ Riff B (1st 7 meas.)
(A5)
(D5)
(B7(no3rd))
Roll - er coast - er, fa - v'rite ride. Let me kiss you one last
Interlude
Half-time feel
Gtr. 2 tacet
(D5)
A5
Rhy. Fig. 1
Gtr. 1
time.
Gtr. 2
Riff C
Gtr. 3 (dist.)
f
E5
D5
2nd time, End half-time feel
End Rhy. Fig. 1
End Riff C

Verse
3rd time, Gtr. 3 tacet
A5 D5 B5 D5
Rhy. Fig. 2
End Rhy. Fig. 2
Gtr. 1
1. Leave me stand - ing here, Act like I'm not a - round. The
2. Lay be - side me and lis - ten at the wall. We'll
3. Make me prom - ise that I will nev - er tell. All
Gtr. 3
Gtr. 1: w/ Rhy. Fig. 2 (3 times)
1st & 2nd times, Gtr. 3 tacet
coast will prob - 'bly nev - er clear. Can I please go home now? I
keep on ly - ing un - til the sum - mer comes. I
I re - mem - ber is the way her bed - room smelled. I
had that dream a - bout you a - gain, where I
had that dream a - bout you a - gain, where you
had that dream a - bout you a - gain, where I
To Coda
1.
Half-time feel
Gtrs. 1 & 3 : w/ Rhy. Fig. 1 and Riff C
wait out - side un - til you let me in, and there I stayed.
drive my car right off a fuck - ing cliff.
wait out - side un - til you let me in.
E5
End half-time feel
2.
And now I'm
Chorus
Gtr. 2: w/ Riff B (2 times)
N.C.(A5)
breath - ing deep - ly, walk - ing back - wards,
Gtr. 1

Half-time feel
Gtr. 1 tacet
(D5)
(B7(no3rd))
(D5)
(A5)
find - ing strength to call and ask her. Roll - er coast - er
(D5)
(B7(no3rd))
D5
fa - v'rite ride Let me kiss you one last time.
Interlude
Gtrs. 1 & 2
w/ synth. effects
N.C.(A5)
* Gtr. 4
Gtrs. 1 & 2 tacet
N.C.(A5)
mf
* Bass arr. for gtr.
1.
2.
D.S. al Coda
End half-time feel
(E5)
(D5)
Gtr. 1
P.S.
Coda
Outro-Chorus
w/ synth. effects (till end)
D5
N.C.(A5)
And now I'm breath - ing deep - ly,
Rhy. Fig. 3
Gtr. 1

D5
walk - ing back - wards, find - ing

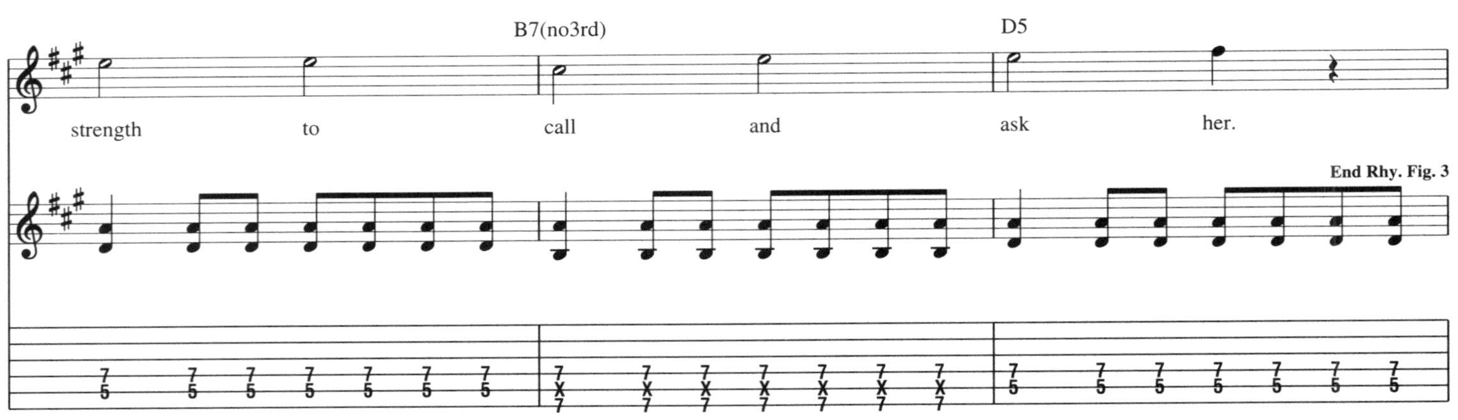
B7(no3rd)
D5
strength to call and ask her.
End Rhy. Fig. 3

Gtr. 1: w/ Rhy. Fig. 3
N.C.(A5)
D5
Roll - er coast - er, fa - v'rite ride. Let me

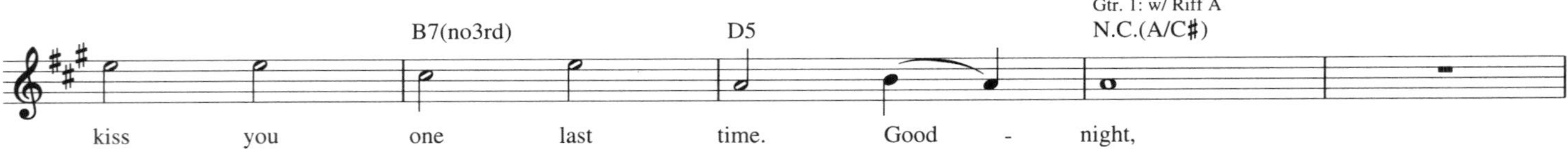
B7(no3rd)
D5
Gtr. 1: w/ Riff A
N.C.(A/C♯)
kiss you one last time. Good - night,

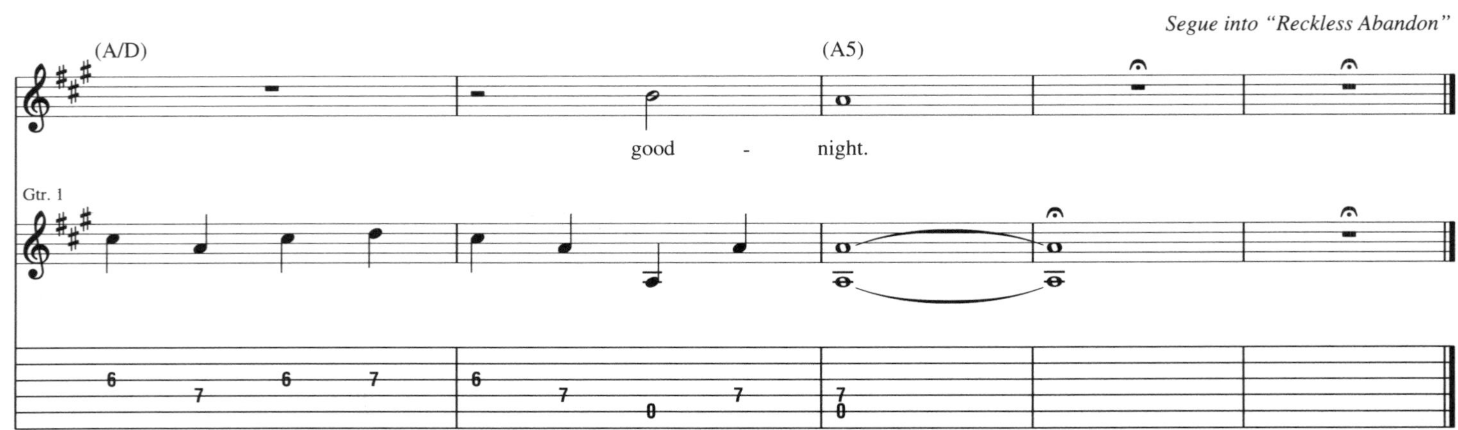
Segue into "Reckless Abandon"
(A/D)
(A5)
good - night.
Gtr. 1

Reckless Abandon

Words and Music by Tom De Longe, Mark Hoppus and Travis Barker

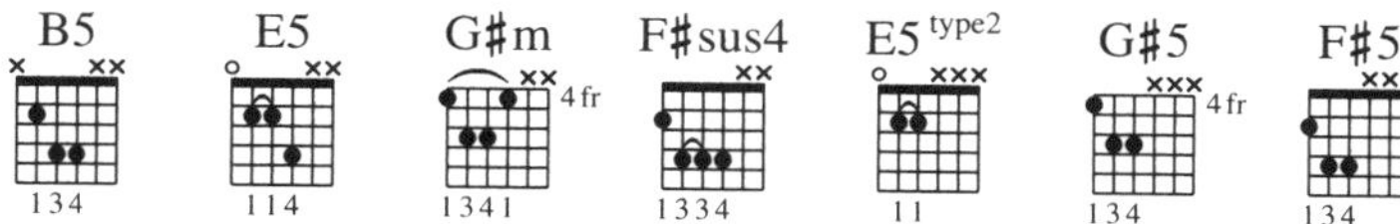

B5
E5
G♯m
F♯sus4
E5 type2
G♯5
F♯5

Chorus
Fast Rock ♩ = 248
B5
E5
On and on, reck - less a - ban - don. Some - thing's
Gtr. 1 (semi-clean)
mf

G♯m
wrong, this is gon - na shock them. Noth - ing to

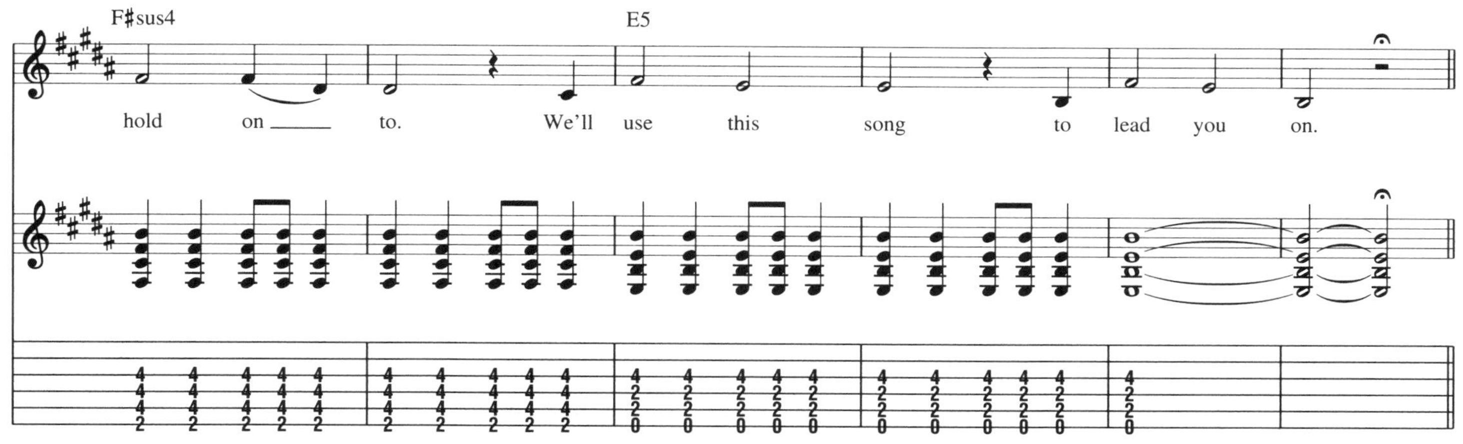

F♯sus4
E5
hold on to. We'll use this song to lead you on.

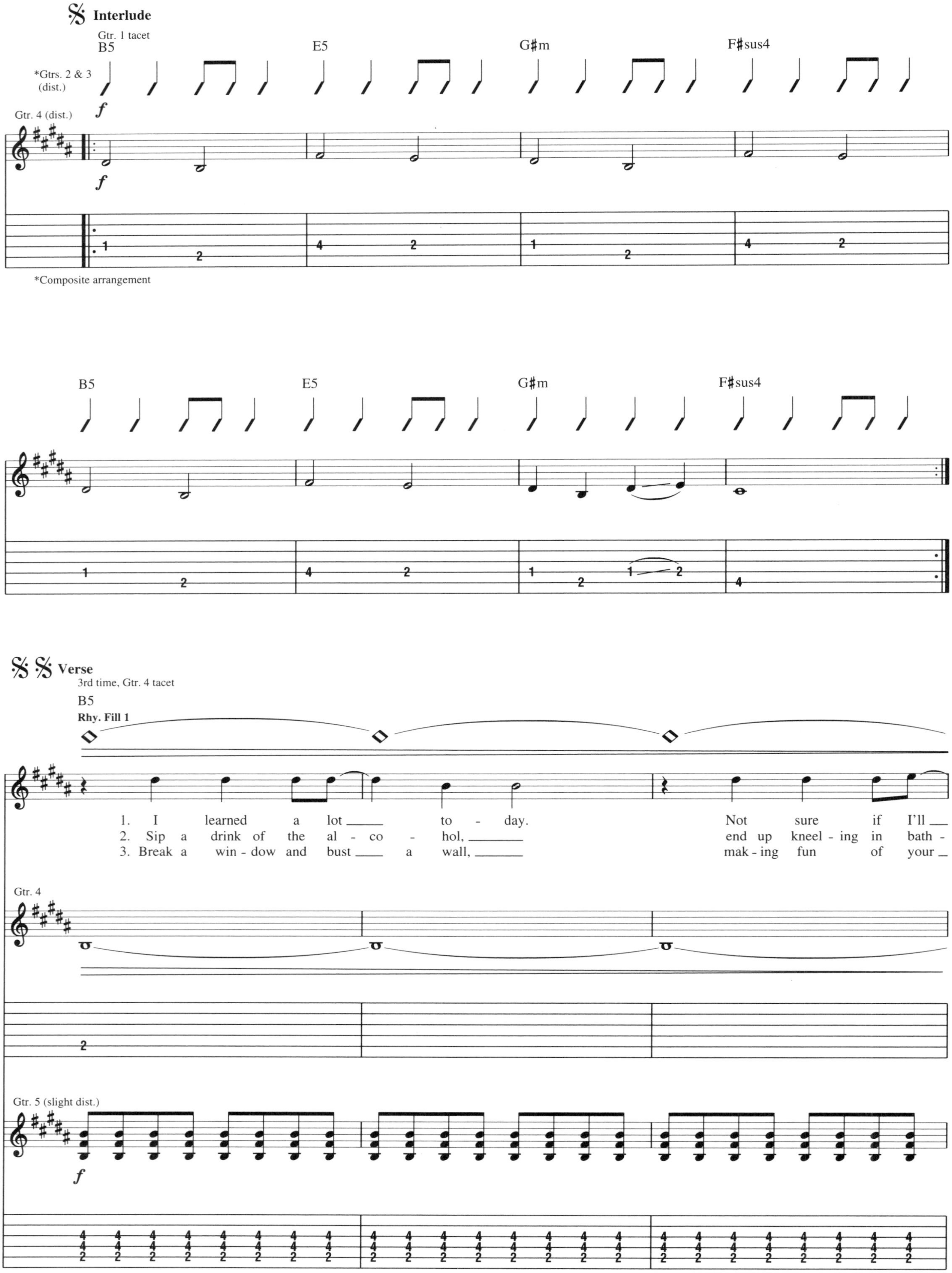

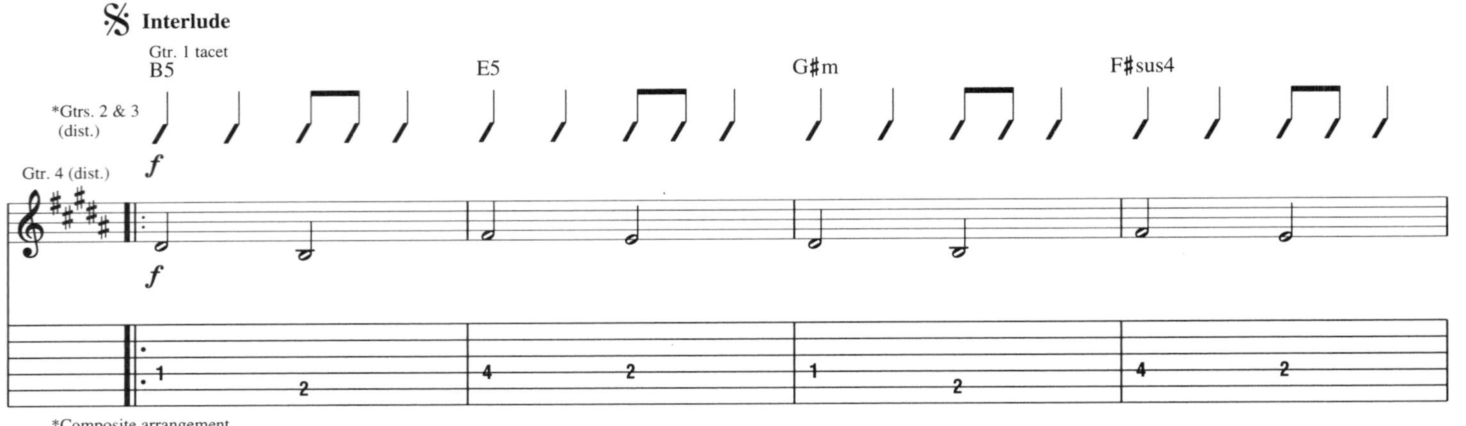

*Composite arrangement

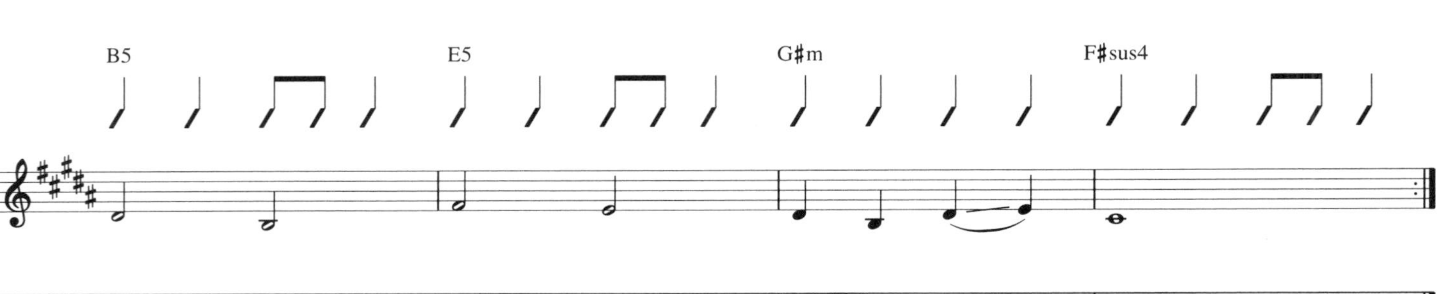

Verse

3rd time, Gtr. 4 tacet

B5

Rhy. Fill 1

1. I learned a lot ___ to - day. Not sure if I'll ___
2. Sip a drink of the al - co - hol, ______ end up kneel - ing in bath -
3. Break a win - dow and bust ___ a wall, ______ mak - ing fun of your ___

Gtr. 4

Gtr. 5 (slight dist.)

f

Gtrs. 2, 3 & 4 tacet
B5/F#
End Rhy. Fill 1
get laid and not sure if I'll fail or pass.
room stalls. Eyes are red and my move - ment's slow.
friend's mom. Turn the mu - sic up way too loud.
Kissed ev - 'ry girl in class. Ev - 'ry - bod - y would waste
Too high, got ver - ti - go. He took a shit in the bath -
Charge the piz - za to the house. Ev - 'ry - bod - y would waste
B5
Gtr. 5
it all to have a sum - mer that they could call
- room tub and fed the dog the brown - ie drugs.
it all to have a sum - mer that they could call

3rd time, To Coda 2
2nd time, To Coda 1
B5/F#
N.C.
B5/F#
N.C.
a mem - o - ry that's full ___ of fun, fucked up when it's ___ all done.
Tried hard to not ___ get caught. _ He fucked a chick in a park - ing lot. ___
mem - o - ry that's full ___ of fun,
Chorus
Gtr. 5 tacet
B5
On and ___ on, reck - less a - ban - don.
Gtrs. 2 & 3
Rhy. Fig. 1
E5
Some - thing's wrong, this is gon - na shock them.
G#m
F#sus4
E5
Noth - ing to hold on ___ to. We'll use this

G♯m
song to lead you on and break the truth with
F♯sus4
E5
D.S. al Coda (take repeat)
more bad ___ news. We left a scar, size: ex - tra large.
End Rhy. Fig. 1
(cont. in slashes)
Coda 1
Chorus
Gtrs. 2 & 3, w/ Rhy. Fig. 1
Gtr. 5 tacet
B5
E5
On and ___ on, reck - less a - ban - don. Some - thing's wrong,
G♯m
F♯sus4
this is gon - na shock them. Noth - ing to hold on ___ to. We'll
E5
G♯m
use this song to lead you on and break the truth with
F♯sus4
E5
more bad ___ news. We left a scar, size: ex - tra large.

1., 2., 3.
4.
Interlude
Half-time feel
1st time, Gtr. 2: w/ Rhy. Fill 1
2nd time, Gtr. 2 tacet
D.S.S. al Coda 2
End half-time feel
Coda 2
Gtr. 5 tacet
B5
E5 type2
G♯5
F♯5
F♯5
N.C.
Gtr. 3
Gtr. 5
fucked up when it's all done.
Chorus
Gtrs. 2 & 3: w/ Rhy. Fig. 1
B5
E5
On and on, reck - less a - ban - don. Some - thing's wrong,
G♯m
F♯sus4
this is gon - na shock them. Noth - ing to hold on to. We'll
E5
G♯m
use this song to lead you on and break the truth with
F♯sus4
E5
more bad news. We left a scar, size: ex - tra large.
Gtrs. 2 & 3
B5
mf *
f
*Vol. swell

Everytime I Look for You

Words and Music by Tom De Longe, Mark Hoppus and Travis Barker

Verse
B5
C#5
E5
B5
2. One more point of con - ten - tion, I need some in - ter - ven - tion. Ap-proached with vague in - ten - tions,
3. More time a - part will give you a few more mouth's to ar - gue. Is this too much to live through?
Gtr. 4
Gtrs. 1 & 2
End double-time feel
Pre-Chorus
C#5
E5
B
B/C#
B/E
be - tray my short at - ten - tion... Span the dis - tance, bridge the bor - der.
It al - ways seemed too far to... Drive the point home, send more let - ters.
Riff C1
End Riff C1
w/ clean tone
Riff C
End Riff C
Gtrs. 1 & 2: w/ Riff C
Gtr. 4: w/ Riff C1
Chorus
Double-time feel
* Gtrs. 1 & 2: w/ Riff A (4 times)
B
B/C#
B/E
B5/G#
B5/E
B5
Beg for - give - ness, round the cor - ner.
Pray to - mor - row ends up bet - ter.
Ev - 'ry time I look for you the sun goes down.
** Lower voice tacet this meas. on D.S.
B5/G#
B5/E
B5
B5/G#
And I stum - ble when this whole thing runs a - ground. I left an - oth - er mes - sage, you are

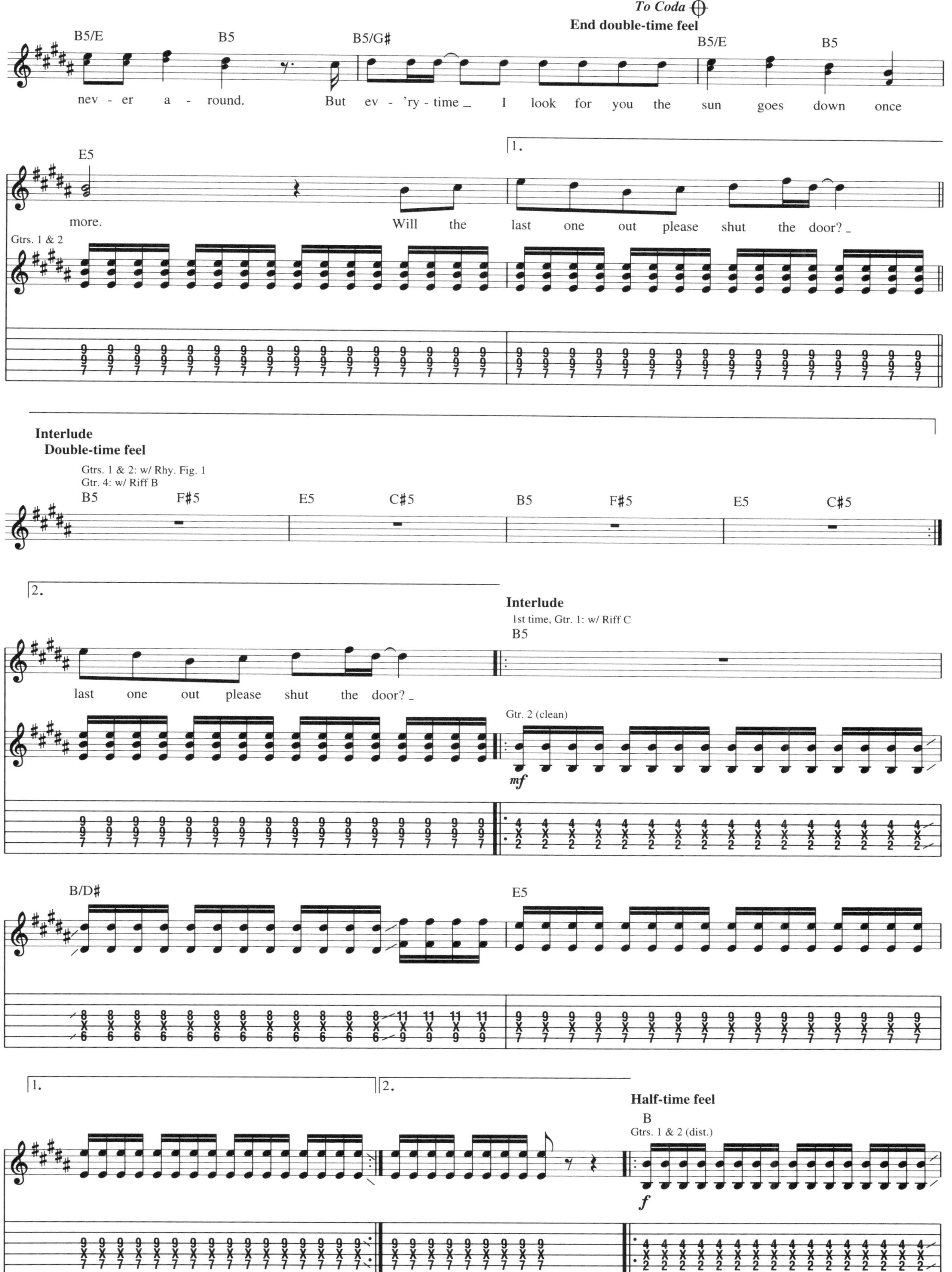
To Coda
End double-time feel
B5/E
B5
B5/G#
B5/E
B5
nev - er a - round. But ev - 'ry - time I look for you the sun goes down once
E5
1.
more. Will the last one out please shut the door?
Gtrs. 1 & 2
Interlude
Double-time feel
Gtrs. 1 & 2: w/ Rhy. Fig. 1
Gtr. 4: w/ Riff B
B5
F#5
E5
C#5
B5
F#5
E5
C#5
2.
Interlude
1st time, Gtr. 1: w/ Riff C
B5
last one out please shut the door?
Gtr. 2 (clean)
mf
B/D#
E5
1.
2.
Half-time feel
B
Gtrs. 1 & 2 (dist.)
f

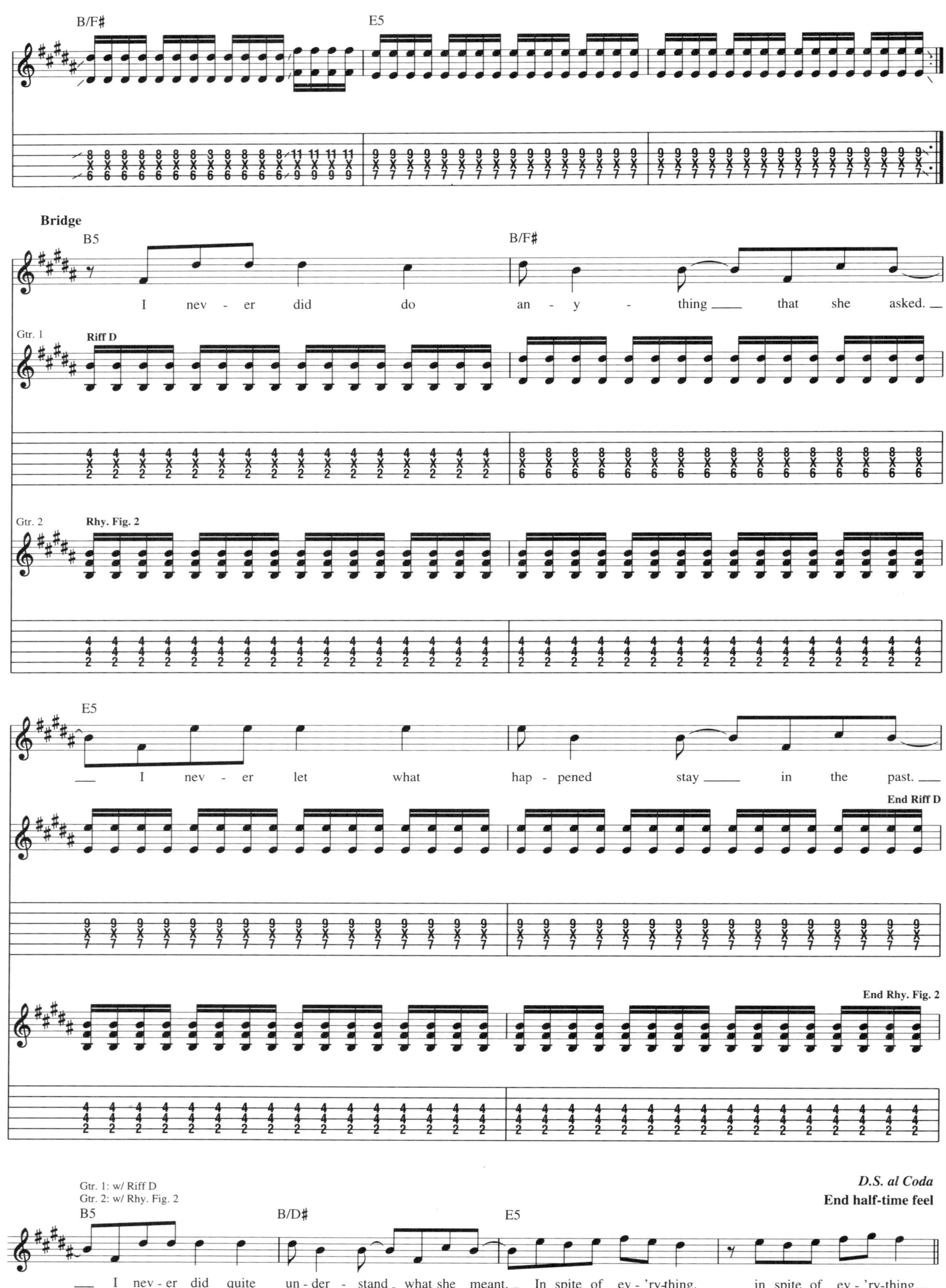
B/F♯
E5
Bridge
B5
B/F♯
I never did do any - thing that she asked.
Gtr. 1
Riff D
Gtr. 2
Rhy. Fig. 2
E5
I never let what happened stay in the past.
End Riff D
End Rhy. Fig. 2
Gtr. 1: w/ Riff D
Gtr. 2: w/ Rhy. Fig. 2
B5
B/D♯
E5
D.S. al Coda
End half-time feel
I nev - er did quite un - der - stand what she meant. In spite of ev - 'ry-thing, in spite of ev - 'ry-thing...

Coda
Double-time feel
Gtrs. 1 & 2: w/ Riff A (2 1/2 times)
B5/E
B5
B5/G♯
B5/E
B5
sun goes down. And I stum - ble when this whole thing runs a - ground. I
Gtr. 4
Gtr. 5 (dist.)
Rhy. Fig. 3
End Rhy. Fig. 3
f
Gtr. 5: w/ Rhy. Fig. 3 (1 1/2 times)
B5/G♯
B5/E
B5
left an - oth - er mes - sage, you are nev - er a - round. But
Gtr. 4
B5/G♯
B/E
E5
ev - 'ry - time I look for you the sun goes down.
Gtr. 4
Gtr. 4
Gtr. 5
divisi
* Gtr. 4 to left of slashes in tab.
Gtrs. 1 & 2

Give Me One Good Reason

Words and Music by Tom De Longe, Mark Hoppus and Travis Barker

E5
(D5)
B5
(A5)
C#5
(B5)
All the kids, they laugh as if they planned it. Why do girls want to
I like the kids who fight a - gainst how they were brought up. They hate the trends and think it's
Heav - y Met-al-ers with their aw - ful, pus - sy hair bands. Count - ing sec - onds un - til
P.M.
A5
(G5)
C#5
(B5)
B5
(A5)
To Coda 1
pierce their nose and walk a - round in torn pan - ty - hose?
fucked to care. It's cool when they piss peo - ple off with what they wear.
we can get a - way, ditch - in' school al - most ev - 'ry sin - gle day.
Oh, yeah.
Interlude
E
(D)
B5
(A5)
N.C.
Rhy. Fig. 1
End Rhy. Fig. 1
Rhy. Fig. 2
End Rhy. Fig. 2
1.
2.
Chorus
3rd time, Gtr. 4 tacet
E/G#
(D/F#)
So give me
3. Give me
one good
Rhy. Fig. 3

B5
(A5)
E5
(D5)
rea - son
why we

E/G#
(D/F#)
B5
(A5)
A5
(G5)
need to
be like them.
End Rhy. Fig. 3

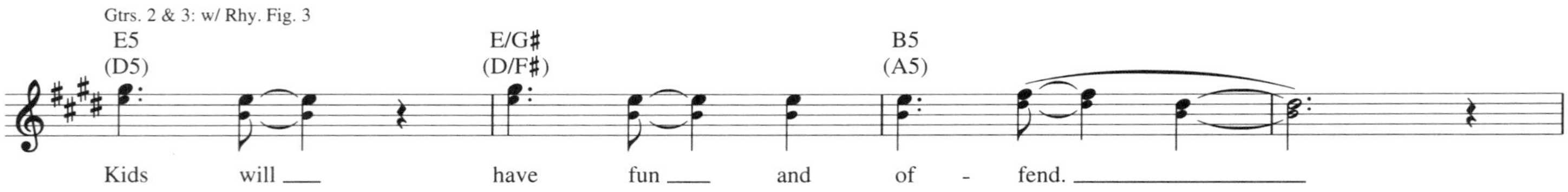
Gtrs. 2 & 3: w/ Rhy. Fig. 3
E5
(D5)
E/G#
(D/F#)
B5
(A5)
Kids will
have fun and
of - fend.

1st time, D.C. al Coda 1
2nd time, to Coda 2
3rd, time, to Coda 3
E5
(D5)
E/G#
(D/F#)
B5
(A5)
A5
(G5)
They don't
want to and
don't fit in.

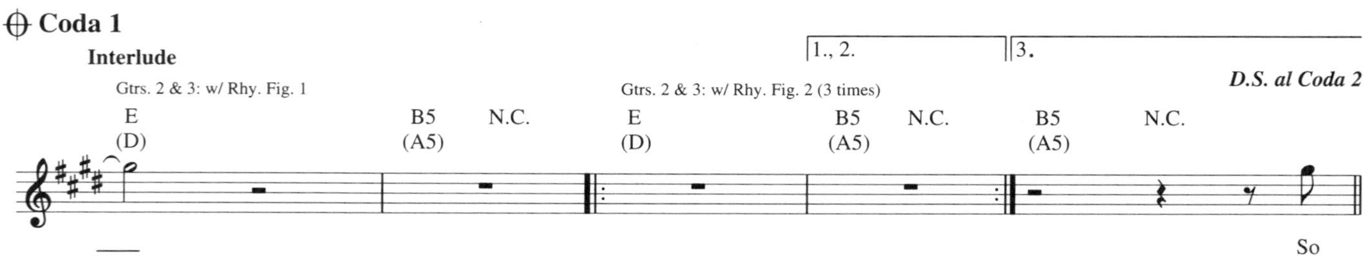
Coda 1
Interlude
1., 2.
3.
D.S. al Coda 2
Gtrs. 2 & 3: w/ Rhy. Fig. 1
Gtrs. 2 & 3: w/ Rhy. Fig. 2 (3 times)
E
(D)
B5
(A5)
N.C.
E
(D)
B5
(A5)
N.C.
B5
(A5)
N.C.
So

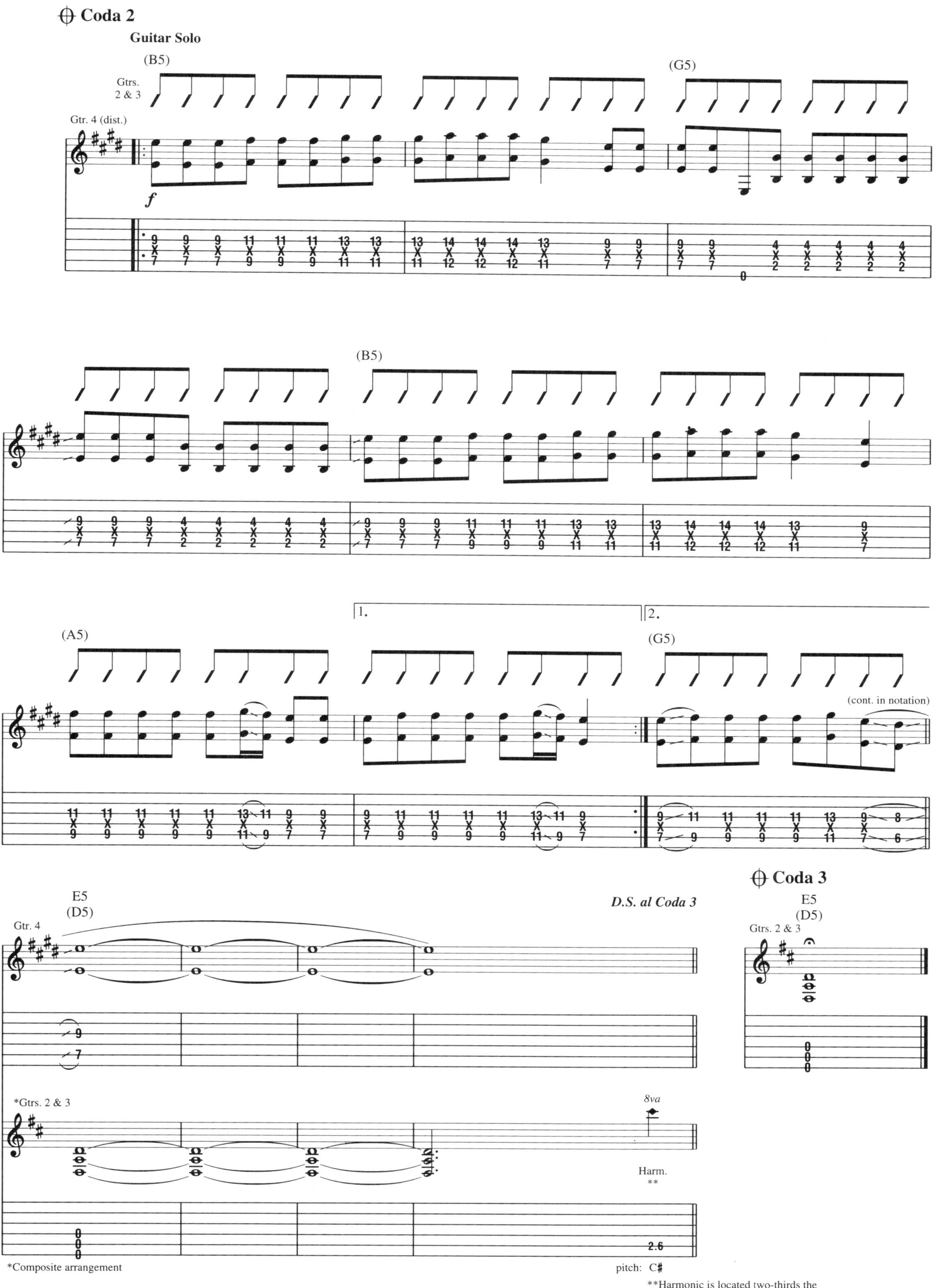
Coda 2
Guitar Solo
(B5)
Gtrs. 2 & 3
(G5)
Gtr. 4 (dist.)
f
(B5)
1.
2.
(A5)
(G5)
(cont. in notation)
E5
(D5)
Gtr. 4
D.S. al Coda 3
Coda 3
E5
(D5)
Gtrs. 2 & 3
*Gtrs. 2 & 3
8va
Harm.
**
*Composite arrangement
pitch: C♯
**Harmonic is located two-thirds the distance between 2nd and 3rd frets.

Shut Up

Words and Music by Tom De Longe, Mark Hoppus and Travis Barker

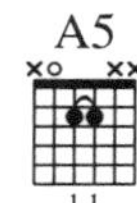

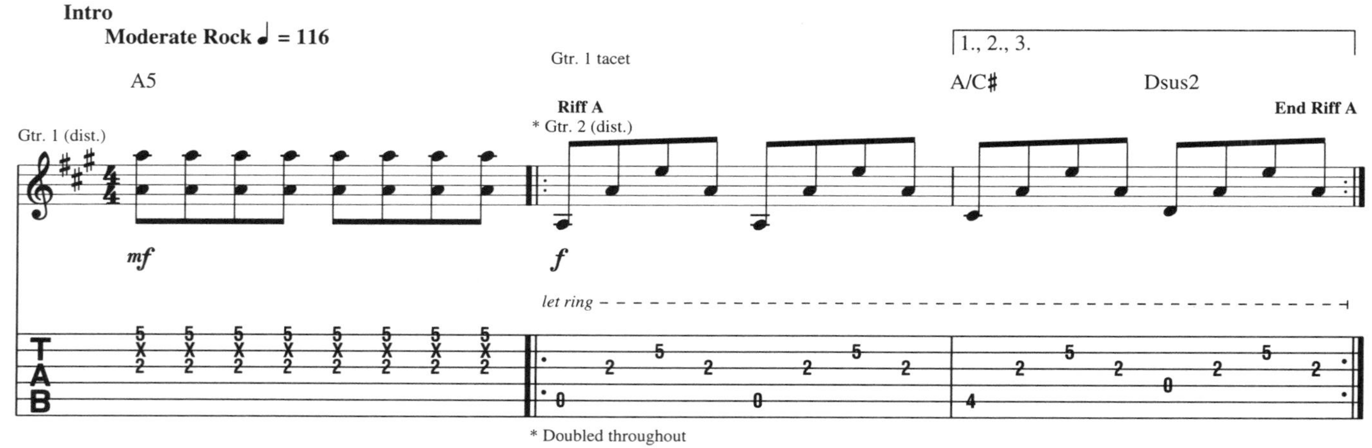

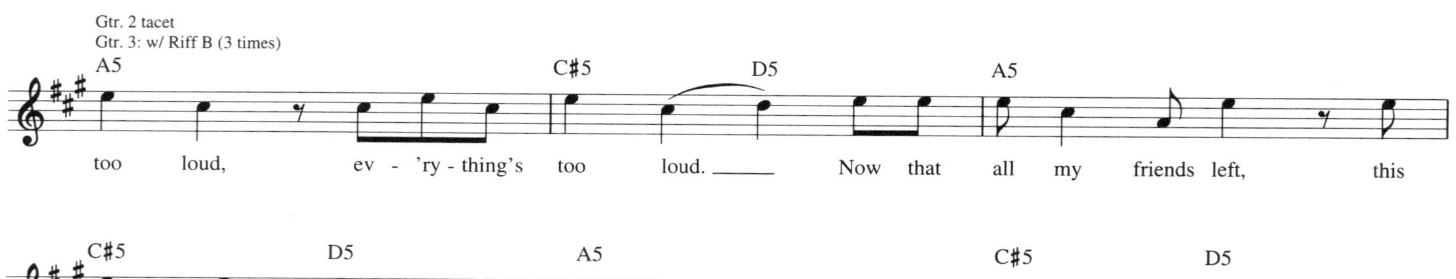

Interlude
Gtr. 1: w/ Riff A
Gtr. 2: w/ Riff A (2 times)
A5
A/C#
Dsus2
A5
A/C#
Dsus2
stop."
I'll run a - way.
(I'll run a - way.)

Verse
Gtr. 2: w/ Rhy. Fill 1
Gtr. 3: w/ Riff B (4 times)
A5
A/C#
Dsus2
A5
C#5
D5
2. "Get the fuck up," she said. "Your life is mean - ing - less, it's go - ing

A5
C#5
D5
A5
no - where, you're go - ing no - where." "You're just a fuck - up," she said. "I'll
(No - where. No - where.)

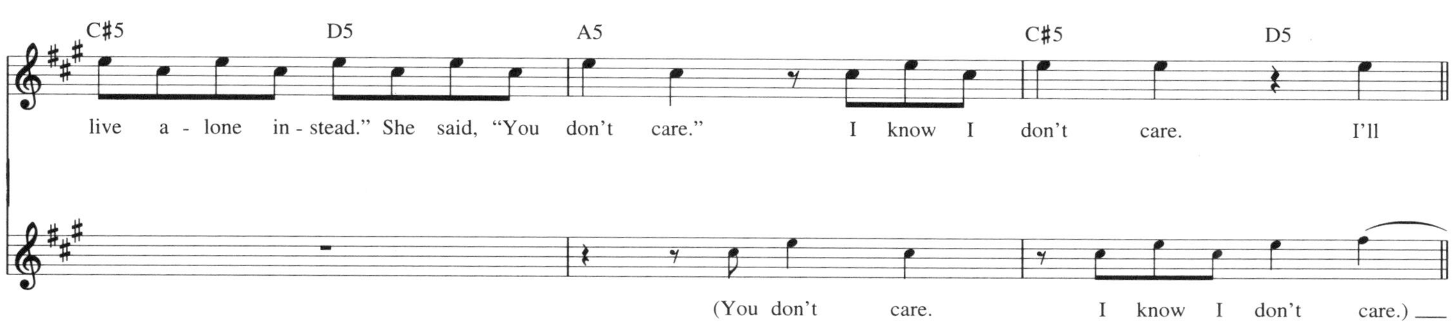
C#5
D5
A5
C#5
D5
live a - lone in - stead." She said, "You don't care." I know I don't care. I'll
(You don't care. I know I don't care.)

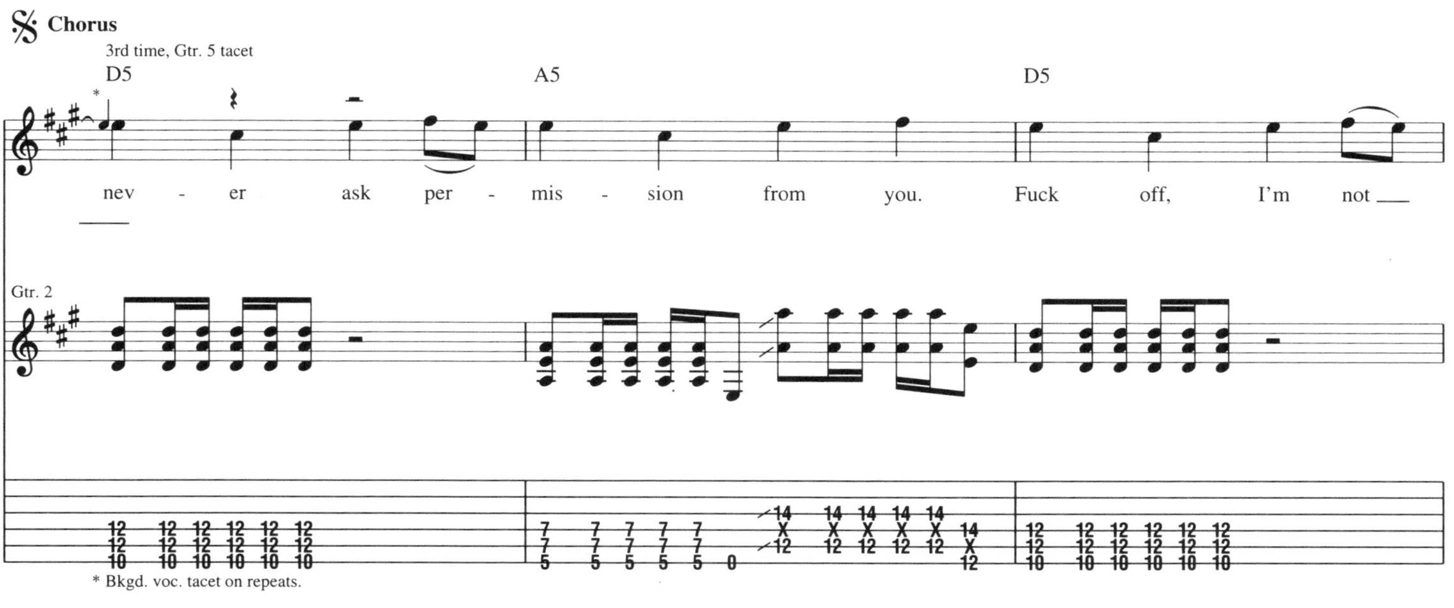
Chorus
3rd time, Gtr. 5 tacet
D5
A5
D5
nev - er ask per - mis - sion from you. Fuck off, I'm not
Gtr. 2
* Bkgd. voc. tacet on repeats.

A5
B5
D5
lis - t'ning to you. I'm not com - ing home. I'm nev - er
To Coda 1
To Coda 2
Verse
B5
D5
A5
go - ing to come back home. 3. I got too fucked-up a - gain and
Rhy. Fill 2
End Rhy. Fill 2
Rhy. Fig. 1
C#5
D5
A5
C#5
D5
passed out on the plane, tried to for - get you, I can't for - get you. No
(For - get you. I can't for - get you.)
End Rhy. Fig. 1

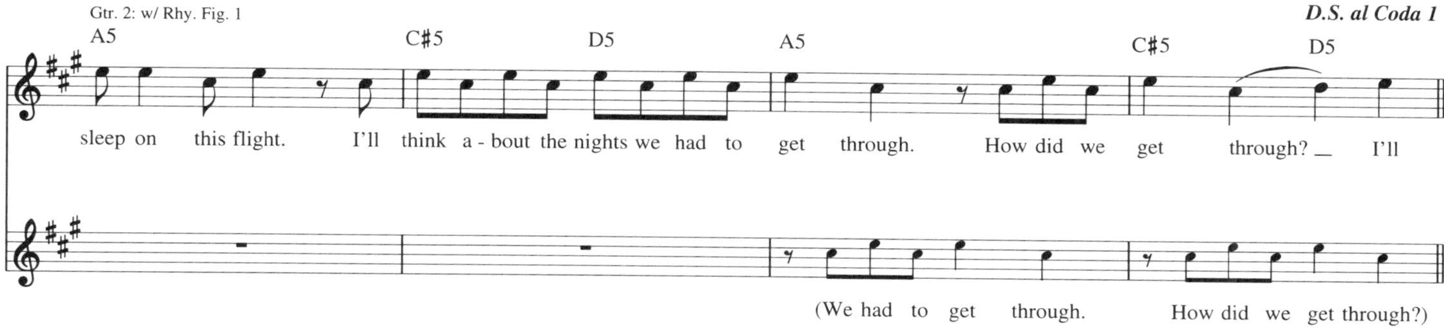

Gtr. 2: w/ Rhy. Fig. 1
D.S. al Coda 1
A5
C#5
D5
A5
C#5
D5
sleep on this flight. I'll think a - bout the nights we had to get through. How did we get through? I'll
(We had to get through. How did we get through?)

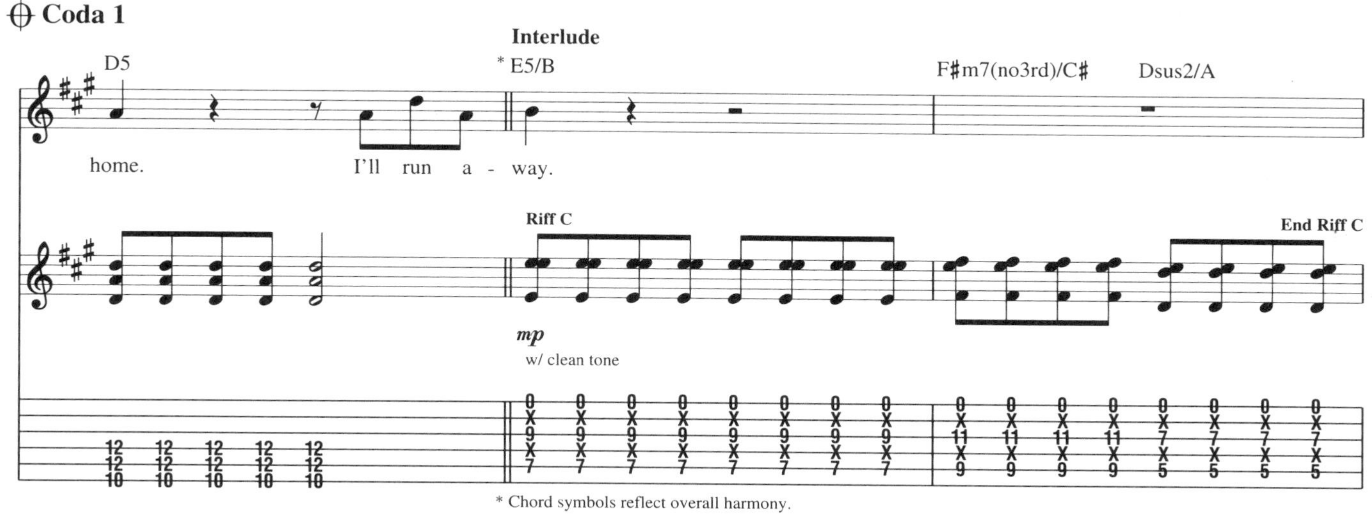

Coda 1
Interlude
D5
* E5/B
F#m7(no3rd)/C#
Dsus2/A
home. I'll run a - way.
Riff C
End Riff C
mp
w/ clean tone
* Chord symbols reflect overall harmony.

Bridge
Gtr. 2: w/ Riff C
Gtr. 2: w/ Riff C (4 times)
E5/B
F#m7(no3rd)/C# Dsus2/A
E5/B
F#m7(no3rd)/C# Dsus2/A
E5/B
I think it's time that I should leave. I think it's

F#m7(no3rd)/C# Dsus2/A
E5/B
F#m7(no3rd)/C# Dsus2/A
E5/B
time that I should leave. I think it's time that I should leave. I think it's

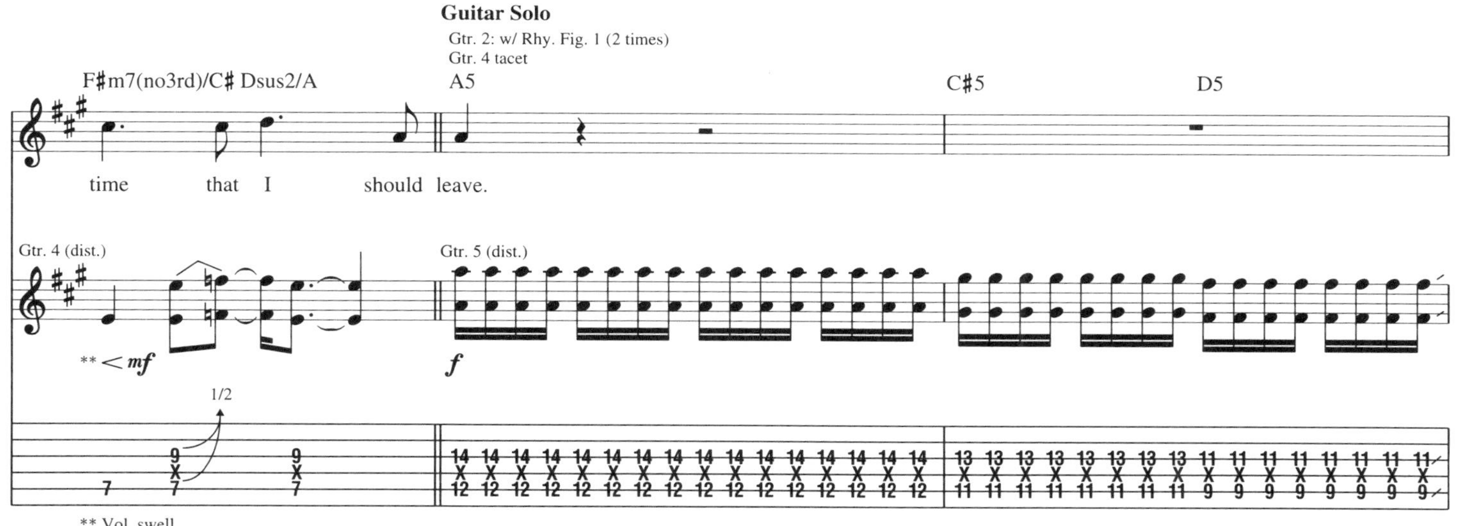

Guitar Solo
Gtr. 2: w/ Rhy. Fig. 1 (2 times)
Gtr. 4 tacet
F#m7(no3rd)/C# Dsus2/A
A5
C#5
D5
time that I should leave.
Gtr. 4 (dist.)
Gtr. 5 (dist.)
mf
f
1/2
** Vol. swell

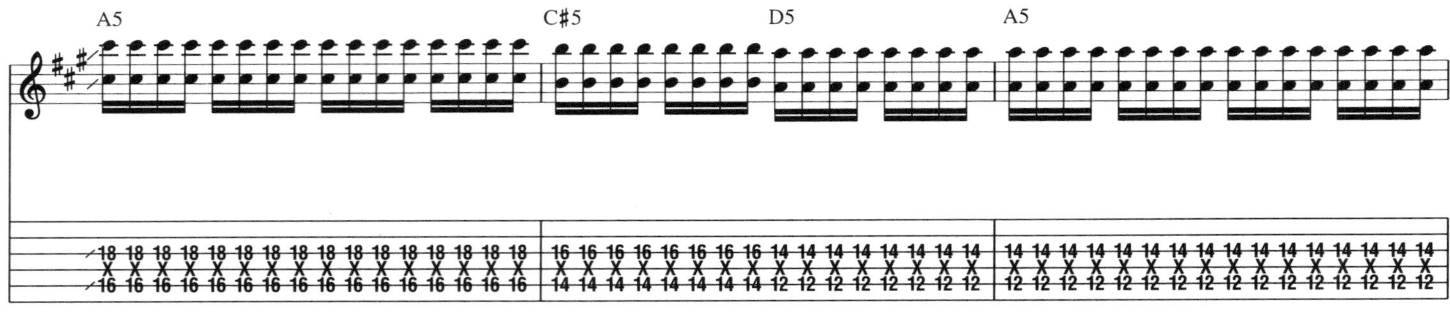
A5
C#5
D5
A5

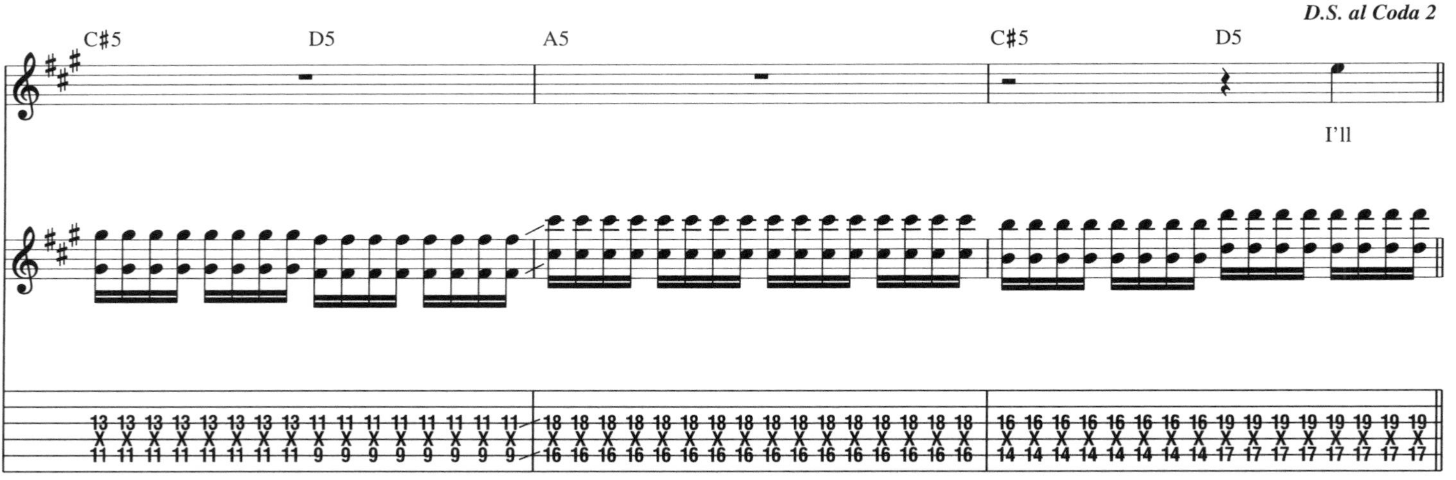
D.S. al Coda 2
C#5
D5
A5
C#5
D5
I'll

Coda 2
Outro
Gtr. 2: w/ Rhy. Fill 2
Gtr. 2: w/ Riff A (3 times)
D5
A5
A/C#
Dsus2
home. I'll run a - way. I think it's time for me to

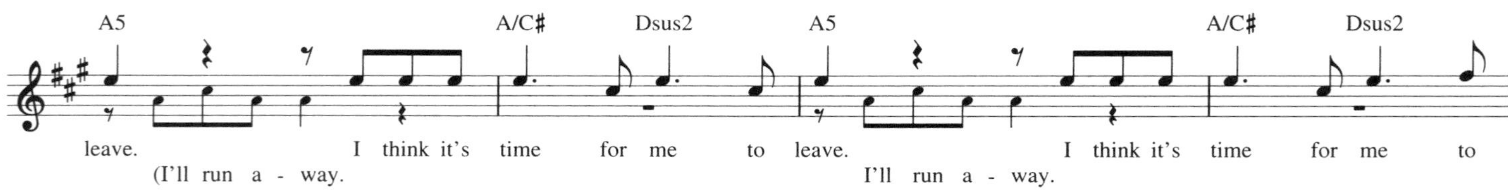
A5
A/C#
Dsus2
A5
A/C#
Dsus2
leave. I think it's time for me to leave. I think it's time for me to
(I'll run a - way. I'll run a - way.

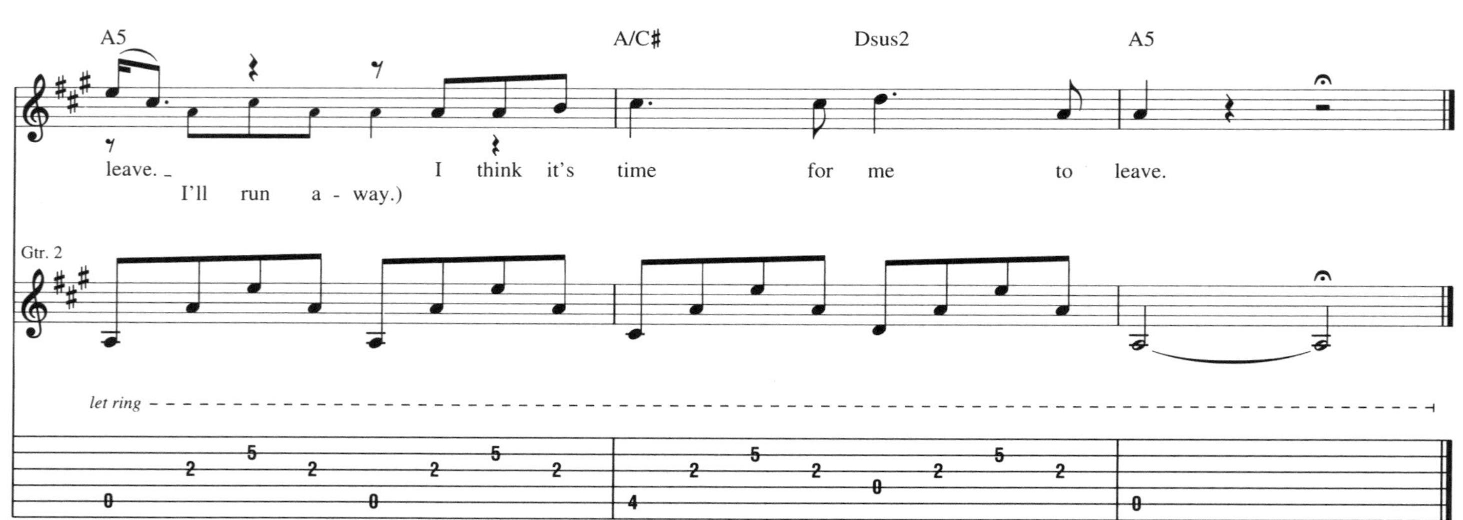
A5
A/C#
Dsus2
A5
leave. I think it's time for me to leave.
I'll run a - way.)
Gtr. 2
let ring

Please Take Me Home

Words and Music by Tom De Longe, Mark Hoppus and Travis Barker

Pre-Chorus
Gtr. 1 tacet
E5
B5
G♯5
She's un - stop - pa - ble, un - pre - dict - a - ble. I'm so jad - ed,
Gtrs. 2 & 3
F♯5
E5
* F♯/A♯
cal - cu - lat - ed. Wrong.
Gtr. 2
Gtr. 3
* Bass plays A♯ till end of meas.
Chorus
B5
F♯/A♯
G♯5
E5
Please take ___ me home. ___ Too late, ___ it's gone. ___
Gtrs. 2 & 3
Rhy. Fig. 2
End Rhy. Fig. 2

To Coda
B5
F#/A#
G#5
E5
I bet you're sad.
This is the best time we ev - er had.
(cont. in slashes)
Verse
Gtrs. 2 & 3
B5
C#5
G#5
E5
mf
P.M.
2. Buy hope, hope that it lasts.
Gtr. 1
mf
Gtr. 1: w/ Riff A (2 times)
Gtrs. 2 & 3: w/ Rhy. Fig. 1 (3 times)
Give in, for - get the past.
Be strong when things fall a - part.
Gtr. 1: w/ Riff B
D.S. al Coda
Hon - est, this breaks my heart.
Coda
This is the best time we ev - er had.
Please take me home.

G#5
E5
B5
F#/A#
Too late, it's gone. I bet you're sad.
G#5
E5
Interlude
B5
C#m
This is the best time we ev - er had.
Gtrs. 2 & 3
Riff C
Gtr. 4 (clean)
mf
B
E5/B
Gtrs. 2 & 3 tacet
B5
C#m
B
E5/B
End Riff C
Bridge
Gtr. 4: w/ Riff C
B5
C#m
B
E5/B
B5
C#m
Why did we have to go date?
It's too eas - y to com - pli - cate.

Double-time feel
B
E5/B
** B5
C#m
B/D#
B/E
Be strong when things fall a - part.
(Be strong when things fall a - part.
Gtrs. 2 & 3
* f P.M.
* Vol. swell ** Chord symbols reflect overall harmony.
B5
C#m
B/D#
B/E
Hon - est, this breaks my heart.
It's so hard.)
Let's go!
P.M.
Interlude
Gtr. 2: w/ Rhy. Fig. 2 (2 times)
Gtr. 3
B5
F#/C#
1.
G#5/D#
E5
2.
G#5/D#
E5
B5 type2
F#/A#
G#5 type2
E5 type2
Gtr. 2
1.

2.
End double-time feel
E5 type2
F♯5
(cont. in notation)
Gtrs. 2 & 3
P.M.
Chorus
Gtrs. 2 & 3: w/ Rhy. Fig. 2 (2 times)
B5
F♯/A♯
G♯5
E5
Please take me home. Too late, it's gone.
I bet you're sad. This is the best time we ev - er had.
B5 type2
G♯5 type2
Please take me home. too late, it's gone.
This is the best time we ev - er had.

2/02

Guitar Notation Legend

Guitar Music can be notated three different ways: on a *musical staff*, in *tablature*, and in *rhythm slashes*.

RHYTHM SLASHES are written above the staff. Strum chords in the rhythm indicated. Use the chord diagrams found at the top of the first page of the transcription for the appropriate chord voicings. Round noteheads indicate single notes.

THE MUSICAL STAFF shows pitches and rhythms and is divided by bar lines into measures. Pitches are named after the first seven letters of the alphabet.

TABLATURE graphically represents the guitar fingerboard. Each horizontal line represents a string, and each number represents a fret.

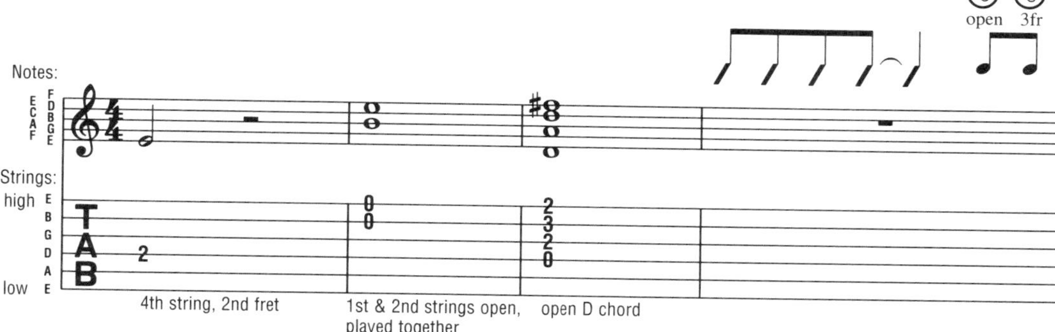

HALF-STEP BEND: Strike the note and bend up 1/2 step.

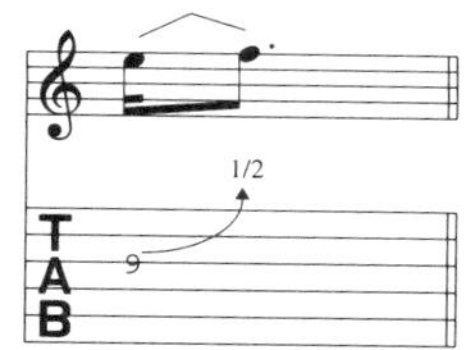

WHOLE-STEP BEND: Strike the note and bend up one step.

GRACE NOTE BEND: Strike the note and immediately bend up as indicated.

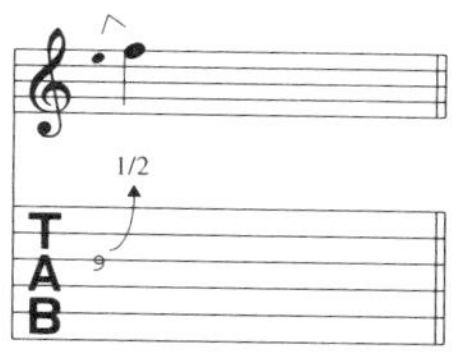

SLIGHT (MICROTONE) BEND: Strike the note and bend up 1/4 step.

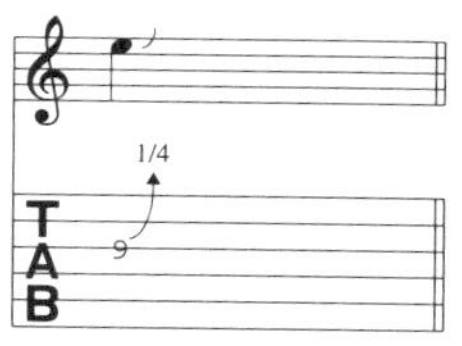

BEND AND RELEASE: Strike the note and bend up as indicated, then release back to the original note. Only the first note is struck.

PRE-BEND: Bend the note as indicated, then strike it.

VIBRATO: The string is vibrated by rapidly bending and releasing the note with the fretting hand.

WIDE VIBRATO: The pitch is varied to a greater degree by vibrating with the fretting hand.

HAMMER-ON: Strike the first (lower) note with one finger, then sound the higher note (on the same string) with another finger by fretting it without picking.

PULL-OFF: Place both fingers on the notes to be sounded. Strike the first note and without picking, pull the finger off to sound the second (lower) note.

LEGATO SLIDE: Strike the first note and then slide the same fret-hand finger up or down to the second note. The second note is not struck.

SHIFT SLIDE: Same as legato slide, except the second note is struck.

TRILL: Very rapidly alternate between the notes indicated by continuously hammering on and pulling off.

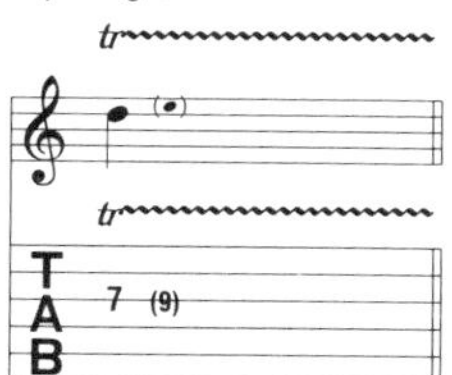

TAPPING: Hammer ("tap") the fret indicated with the pick-hand index or middle finger and pull off to the note fretted by the fret hand.

NATURAL HARMONIC: Strike the note while the fret-hand lightly touches the string directly over the fret indicated.

PINCH HARMONIC: The note is fretted normally and a harmonic is produced by adding the edge of the thumb or the tip of the index finger of the pick hand to the normal pick attack.

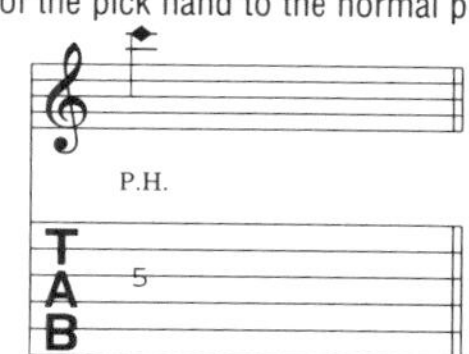

PICK SCRAPE: The edge of the pick is rubbed down (or up) the string, producing a scratchy sound.

MUFFLED STRINGS: A percussive sound is produced by laying the fret hand across the string(s) without depressing, and striking them with the pick hand.

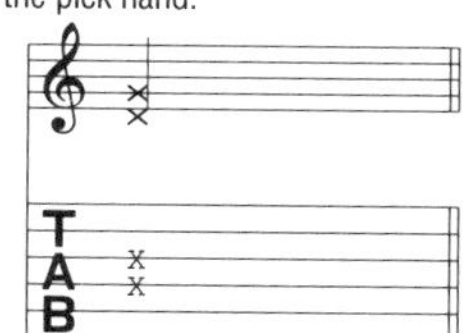

PALM MUTING: The note is partially muted by the pick hand lightly touching the string(s) just before the bridge.

RAKE: Drag the pick across the strings indicated with a single motion.

TREMOLO PICKING: The note is picked as rapidly and continuously as possible.

VIBRATO BAR DIVE AND RETURN: The pitch of the note or chord is dropped a specified number of steps (in rhythm) then returned to the original pitch.

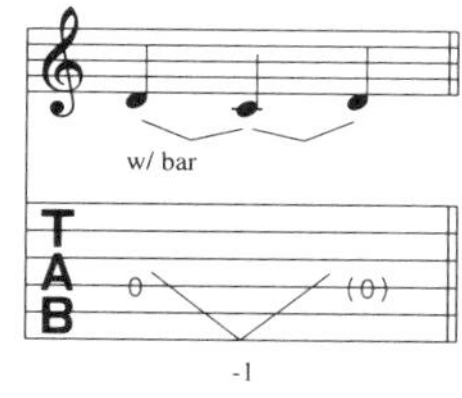

VIBRATO BAR SCOOP: Depress the bar just before striking the note, then quickly release the bar.

VIBRATO BAR DIP: Strike the note and then immediately drop a specified number of steps, then release back to the original pitch.